THE FLOOD RECONSIDERED

THE FLOOD RECONSIDERED

*A review of the evidences of geology, archaeology,
ancient literature and the Bible*

FREDK. A. FILBY
M.Sc., Ph.D.(London), F.R.I.C.

Foreword by
STEPHEN S. SHORT
B.D., M.B., Ch.B.

LONDON
PICKERING & INGLIS LTD
1970

PICKERING & INGLIS LTD.
29 LUDGATE HILL, LONDON, E.C.4
26 BOTHWELL STREET, GLASGOW, C.2

Printed in Great Britain by Robert MacLehose and Co. Ltd. Glasgow

CONTENTS

PREFACE

ENCOURAGED by the kindly reception given to my book on
Genesis 1 in the light of modern science, I have ventured to
proceed to a consideration of Genesis 6–9, the record of the
Flood. The account of the Deluge is one of the most solemn in
all ancient history; the wonderfully detailed story of Noah and
his deliverance, one of the most intriguing of all time.

It may be well here to state clearly what I have, and what I
have not, endeavoured to do. I have not set out to prove that
there was a Flood. For me, the sober historical account in
Genesis, reinforced by the words of Christ, is sufficient. Over
many years I have studied the writings of those who dismiss the Genesis account as a legend which grew out of a
local flood. I have read the views of those who say that the
account is mythical in the sense that it tried, like some of the
Babylonian myths are said to do, merely to teach mankind some
useful lesson. I find myself compelled to reject both of these
views as inadequate. I have listened to the arguments of those
who say that when Christ compared the times of His Second
Coming with the times of judgement in the days of Noah, He
was but sharing the ignorance of His hearers. I have attended
thoughtfully to all such arguments, but I have rejected them
completely. For myself, I still believe that Christ's knowledge of
world history, past, present, and future, vastly exceeded that of
twentieth century theological students who by no means agree
among themselves.

On the positive side, I have tried to show that the Biblical
account is an extremely ancient, very detailed and reliable record
of the experiences of one man who, with his family, alone escaped

vii

from a vast flood which swept across a very large area of Europe
and Asia, and possibly beyond, at a date which lies somewhere
between the end of the Glacial Period and the rise of the great
Empires of the Middle East. The careful study of geology,
climatology, archaeology and ancient literature seems to me to
fall exactly in line with these conclusions.

During more than thirty years' study of ancient chronology
I have watched with interest the constantly shifting dates given
by experts to ancient events, but, despite some hundred pages
of notes, I have felt compelled at present to leave a wide margin
in the date of the Flood.

I have tried to give facts wherever possible, and to quote the
findings of those who are experts in their own fields, so that the
reader may form his own final judgement, but in several places
I have assumed an author's right to give his own conclusions.
The references and some additional pieces of information are
placed at the ends of the chapters.

My thanks are due to my wife, Mrs. F. A. Filby, B.A., for
considerable help with the legends of various nations. I am
grateful to Dr. Stephen S. Short for many helpful suggestions,
to Mr. D. F. Payne, M.A., for information concerning several
Hebrew words, to Mr. Travers Harpur, LL.B., for obtaining
useful information about the Ararat region and to Mr. R. B.
Randall for details of fossils in the Andes. I am grateful, too, to
the Redbridge librarians for their help in obtaining a number of
useful books.

FOREWORD

I esteem it a pleasure, and indeed a privilege, to have been asked by my friend Dr. Filby to write a Foreword to this latest book of his, 'The Flood Reconsidered'. It is a valuable work in three respects, firstly in that it furnishes ample evidence, from many sources, of the historicity of the deluge in the time of Noah, secondly in that it provides an enlightening exposition of the Bible's account of this event, and thirdly in that it draws attention to the significance of the story for the present generation.

This last matter is of immense importance, and the more so because it is so often overlooked. Rightly does the author call attention to the words of the Lord Jesus: 'As it was in the days of Noah, even so shall it be also in the days of the Son of Man. They ate, they drank, they married, they were given in marriage, until the day that Noah entered the ark, and the flood came and destroyed them all.' (Luke 17. 26–27).

One's desire and prayer with regard to this book is that it might promote in its readers a firmer confidence in the truthfulness of God's Word, and that it might impel them to prepare themselves, in accordance with New Testament teaching, against that 'judgment to come' which the Flood described in Genesis so graphically foreshadows.

STEPHEN S. SHORT

CHAPTER 1

SCIENTIFIC ASPECTS OF THE FLOOD

THE work which follows will be divided into four sections:
(1) The evidence provided by the various sciences, including the
findings of archaeologists (2) The Flood records of many nations,
ancient and modern, and including those discovered in excavations (3) A detailed study of the Biblical account and (4) Some
practical observations and conclusions.

In dealing, in this chapter, with the scientific aspects of the
question, we shall again divide the study into three sections:
(I) The fact of great floods in ancient times, and especially
around the most probable time for the Genesis Flood (II) The
possible causes of such floods and (III) The probable extent and
time of Noah's Flood.

Since the fact that great areas of land have experienced devastating floods in the past is so well known to geologists, and
seeing that a vast tract of land was submerged by the Deluge in
the time of Noah is so clearly asserted by the Bible, there should
be considerable agreement on the first point. There will be much
greater scope for discussion on the second topic particularly as
some of the factors involved are still not fully understood. The
third section will lead to the interesting problem as to which of
the ancient floods recorded by geology and by archaeology
coincides with that of Genesis. It may be worth stating now that
the second and third sections are of great academic interest, but
the conclusions are not vital to our belief in the Genesis account.

I

We turn our attention first to the question of large floods in
general. All geologists are familiar with the facts, but it may

interest the reader who has not had an opportunity to study that branch of science to examine the evidence. Considering for a moment the entire scope of geological history, doubtless many hundreds of millions of years, we find that whole continents and mountain masses have been under water several times. One, out of many dozens of extracts that might be quoted, must suffice for this point. Prof. Joly in his work, *The Surface-History of the Earth*, pp. 85 and 107, says, 'The surface-history of the Earth has by no means been uniform and monotonous. Great physical changes have been repeated at intervals. It would appear as if six great cycles of world-transforming events are recognizable during the course of geological history. In each of these cycles the succession of events has been the same. The continents sink relatively to the ocean. The waters flow in over the lower levels and vast areas become covered by the transgressional seas . . . the most striking fact known about the mountains is that they are largely and often mainly composed of sedimentary rocks, that is, of rocks which have been deposited originally in the seas. True, these sediments may be contorted, folded, even metamorphosed almost beyond recognition, but none the less they have risen from the sea-floor to form the mountain chain. It is a universal fact. Even of the volcano-topped Andes and Caucasus it is true . . . the hard slates, telling of former deep waters, buttress such giants as the Eiger or the Matterhorn, and often overlie, or intermingle with, the granites of the Himalayas.' The reference here to the Caucasus is interesting especially as geological maps of ancient times also show that the Black Sea, the Caspian and the Sea of Aral formed one vast ocean with the Caucasus then standing up as a great island.[1]

Some of these movements were very gradual, taking thousands of years, but others, like the outpouring of thousands of millions of tons of lava to cover 200,000 square miles of the Deccan, were much more rapid. For the moment all we are concerned to show is that vast areas of the Earth can be submerged, and this we can consider proved.

Towards the end of the vast geological ages there settled over the northern and southern regions of the Earth huge areas of ice. The period in question, known as the Glacial Period, of uncertain length, came to an end with the melting of a considerable amount of ice, and the retreat of the glaciers mainly to Arctic regions and a few mountain masses like those of Norway and Switzerland. This melting of the ice is believed to have raised the level of the oceans by some 300 feet. It is generally conceded that the Ice Age ended about 10,000 years ago, although the date must necessarily be somewhat vague. The geological periods involved are divided and named as follows. The whole period is called the Quaternary Period and this is sub-divided into the earlier part which includes the Ice Age itself, known as the Pleistocene, and the period which followed the main retreat of the ice, which is called the Recent. Since by general consensus of opinion the Genesis Flood occurred after the end of the Ice Age we must inquire whether great earth-movements grew less or slower in the Pleistocene and particularly in the Recent periods. The result of such an inquiry is very surprising. These movements did not get slower or less. In fact they increased to a tremendous crescendo. Some maintain that these changes were more violent than any in the previous great cycles mentioned by Prof. Joly.

Let us listen first to Prof. Lester King of Natal University who, in his very recent work, *The Morphology of the Earth*, p. 33, says, 'A large extension of South-East Asia has recently sunk beneath the sea until only islands and peninsulas (Borneo, Sumatra, Java, Malaya) remain visible where formerly land was continuous. So *recent* is the subsidence, that drowned river valleys can still be integrated into a former drainage system, and the distribution of river-fish upon the islands still follows the former hydrography. The whole sea-board of Eastern Asia is, indeed, drowned in various degrees, and the true margin of the Asiatic block is to be traced along the island festoons which are so marked a feature of that region. The Sea of Japan is a deeply subsided basin, the East China and Yellow Seas are really shelf, covered by less than one hundred fathoms of water. These inundations have doubtless

been caused by subsidence of the continental mass.' Prof.
King adds, 'The greatest uplift has taken place in the Himalaya
. . . the modern Andes were created by violent Pleistocene up-
arching. There is, of course, much evidence of a very late
vertical movement of the Himalaya . . . from Tibet into Europe
the mountain garland, Hindu Kush, Elburz, and Caucasus is
everywhere the product of uplift during Pliocene to Recent
times . . . volcanic activity built huge cones of andesite or
trachyte with basalt . . . e.g. the mountains of Ararat and
Demavend.'[2] Clearly then the Quaternary Era was marked by
very great geological movement and this continued beyond the
end of the Glacial Period into the so-called Recent times. With
this Prof. Charlesworth fully agrees. In fact he goes even further.
In his massive two-volume work, *The Quaternary Era with
special reference to its glaciation*,[3] he says, 'The Pleistocene indeed
witnessed earth-movements on a considerable, even catastrophic
scale. There is evidence that it created mountains and ocean
deeps of a size previously unequalled . . . the Pleistocene indeed
represents one of the crescendi in the earth's tectonic history.
The movements affected about forty million square kilometres
of the continents and 330 million square kilometres of the ocean
floor, i.e. 70 per cent of the total surface of the earth. Asia was
subjected to powerful and far-reaching disturbances; the fault
troughs of the Dead Sea, Red Sea, Jordan Valley,[4] Gulf of Aden,
Persian Gulf, and Arabian Sea received their present form.
Earth-movements elevated the Caucasus; the amount since
Mindel time (i.e. the second stage of the Ice Age) is estimated at
3900 feet . . . and raised the Lake Baikal region (Lake Baikal
itself was deepened) and Central Asia by 6700 feet. The
Himalayas were also increased in height by 6700 feet. Similar
changes took place around the Pacific and in North China the
uplift was estimated as 10,000 feet.' Many other quotations
could be given to show that it is established beyond any
reasonable doubt by geological research that great risings and
fallings of huge areas of land took place during and after the end
of the Ice Age. Some of these vast movements belong to the

Recent period, i.e. within the last 10,000 years where, on any count, the Flood of Noah belongs. Our first point then is established. Far from the Genesis Flood being an unlikely event in recent geological times it fits quite naturally into such a period ... in fact it was the most likely period for such a rapid and violent upheaval. The wonder, one might say, was not so much that it happened, but that it should be pronounced by God in Genesis as the last such flood, never to be repeated on that scale again. And this has been true. After crowding such a number of violent changes into the Glacial Period and continuing them into the relatively few thousand years between the Ice Age and the rise of the great dynasties and empires, the earth seems almost suddenly to have settled down to a period of comparative stability during what we might call Historical times. Almost all movements since then have been either very slow or restricted to a small area. Such final adjustments, or shudders, like the aftermaths of earthquakes, continue to this day. They are responsible for the lesser raised beaches of Scotland, the rise and fall of the Fens, for sunken harbours once used by ships, for most of the rises and falls of the Mesopotamian area,[5] and the Persian Gulf, and the even slower risings and fallings of parts of our English coasts. These, we would repeat, are but small adjustments after the great earth-movements of the Quaternary and it is these great movements that at present occupy our attention.

Let it be again stressed that we are NOT now dealing with gradual changes spread over thousands or millions of years in the past although we do not question that such happened. We are providing evidence of great earth-movements and flooding within a period of at most a few thousand years between the end of the Ice Age and the rise of the great empires.

Beds of sand and gravel with RECENT shells can be found on Moel Tryfan at a height of 1350 feet showing that N. Wales was plunged beneath the sea at no great time past, and has risen again.[6] The shells in the quarry at the top of the Great Orme are not fossilized. Darwin was surprised to find that shells 1300 feet up in the Andes were not fossilized. So far as he could see the coast there had risen by that amount, not in millions or even thousands of years. Prof. Prestwich who examined a large number of recent deposits throughout Europe protests emphatically against those who assert that all changes must be slow.[7] Even the most ardent uniformitarians now admit that at times changes take place with catastrophic rapidity. In our own area of Western Europe there is considerable evidence of a vast flood well after the end of the Ice Age, but also well before historical times. This is the Flandrian Transgression or Flood.[8] According to Prof. Austin Miller[9] this took place when the sea-level was high, when the main raised beaches of Norway, Spitzbergen, Franz Joseph Land, Greenland, and some in Scotland were formed, when there was considerable climatic change and when the Caspian and Aral Seas were filled. If we accept these statements and the date of the Flandrian Trangression which is usually put at 6000 to 4000 B.C. we see that such a flood must have occurred at about the same time as many students would date Noah's Flood. The present writer believes that either the Flandrian Transgression in Western and Northern Europe, the great changes in the Sahara,[10] the Genesis Flood as described by Noah in the Middle East, and the sudden coming of the Great Cold to Siberia, leading to the extinction of the mammoth and literally a hundred million other creatures, were parts of a series of catastrophes spread across the ancient world causing the disappearance of the early races of man . . . or they all belong to one event.

The reader is left to form his own conclusions from the evidence already given and more yet to be provided. So far as our main argument is concerned it is sufficient that geological research established the existence of great floods over vast areas within the period to which the Genesis Flood is usually assigned.

II

We turn now to the second aspect of the problem. What are the causes of great floods, and which of these may have operated in the time of Noah? Here, to start with, we have a very simple, almost naïve answer: either the land sinks or the water level rises . . . or both. To quote one who was a life-long student of geology, 'The question as to where the water came from and where it went to will only trouble those who hold extreme views as to the fixity of oceanic and continental levels. If the sea-beds can rise and the continents sink there is no difficulty whatever in finding enough water even for a universal flood.'[11] When we remember that if the whole Earth were perfectly flat the oceans would cover it to a depth of $1\frac{1}{2}$ miles this statement is obviously true. But if we pursue this answer one stage further we find ourselves faced with much that is interesting although little that is absolutely certain.

That land can rise or sink we have already demonstrated. Many of these movements are gradual, due largely to the fact that continents are embedded in a slightly plastic or deformable underlayer in which, by Archimedes' principle, they 'float' like icebergs with the majority of their mass, or foundations, down below. Two main factors seem to operate—the lightening of continents by weathering or the removal of ice loads, and possible movements in the basaltic underlayers. Whilst such movements are generally extremely slow there is evidence, some of which we have already given, that at times they can become much more violent. Further, just as after earthquakes and volcanic eruptions there are usually many minor adjustments, so it seems from geological and historical observations that after the great earth-movements of the Pleistocene and Recent, there have been many lesser movements occasioning local floods.

But floods can also be caused by the rising of the sea-level, and this seems to be indicated clearly by the Biblical account. Two possible factors are there mentioned. Using the picturesque metaphors of ancient languages it records that the *windows* of heaven were opened and the *fountains* of the Great Deep were broken up.[12] In other words, Noah was conscious of torrential rain and the oncoming of a huge tide, not from swollen rivers, but from the great Deep, the ocean. That the latter was much

B

greater than the former is clearly shown by the fact that the Ark
(both in the Biblical and the Babylonian accounts) was carried
northwards towards Armenia, whereas a river flood would have
carried it out to the Persian Gulf.

The actual contribution of rain is not in any case very large.[13]
If all the water in the entire atmosphere was condensed and
spread over the whole world it would probably represent no
more than a few inches. Torrential rain, concentrated in relatively
small areas, particularly valleys, might easily lead to floods of
many feet. If augmented by the presence of large rivers or lakes
they may cover—as has happened in China—hundreds of
square miles, and that to a depth of many feet. Prof. Mallowan,
in a paper published in 1964, seemed to think that the Genesis
Flood was a relatively small affair caused only by rain and
swollen rivers.[14] As R. L. Raikes pointed out in the same
Journal, Mallowan has overlooked the clear statement in Genesis
that the 'Great Deep' played its part, and he himself returns to
the idea of land subsidence as being the chief factor, with the
obvious incoming flood from the Persian Gulf.[15] As we have
already said the direction of drift of the Ark fully agrees with this.

We shall look next at the suggestions that have been made
concerning possible rises in the ocean levels themselves. Four
sources have been suggested—ice, subterranean water, the
collapse of some vapour canopy or ring system like that of Saturn,
and some huge tide that rose and died away.

When the Ice Age ended the great glaciers began to melt and
huge quantities of water and great ice-floes were returned to the
oceans. It is believed that the net result was the raising of the
ocean-levels by as much as 300 feet. This change probably took
many years but the removal of such a weight of ice from northern
lands would set up isostatic strains such as we have already
described, and the lands would adjust themselves, probably not
entirely uniformly, causing numerous earthquakes. These
changes were almost certainly not completely over by the time
of the Genesis Flood and seeing that any change in ocean level
could not be confined to Northern latitudes but must extend

world wide, they must be admitted as a possible secondary factor.

Of the supply of water from the rocks below the continents we know very little. At present it consists of a mere trickle—about a cubic mile of what is called 'juvenile water' each year, coming mainly from volcanoes and geysers. The rock olivine which is plentiful below the continents can, under certain circumstances, take up to 13 per cent water to become the beautiful rock serpentine. Conversely serpentine when heated will give up its 13 per cent water. But how much serpentine there is—or was— below the continents we do not really know. If any large contribution was ever made by this means—and it is difficult to see how it could have been returned again—the water must have been boiling, steam, in fact. Only in one or two most unlikely legends was it ever suggested that the Flood was hot!

The third suggested source for the water of the Flood has been a vast vapour canopy or collection of rings of ice-particles like those of Saturn, which collapsed on to the Earth at the time of the Deluge. Prof. Ramm mentions several works that advocate this theory, but it is at present set out in two rather large works, *The Genesis Flood* by Henry M. Morris and John C. Whitcomb, Jr., and *The Biblical Flood and the Ice Epoch* by Donald Wesley Patten. The former of these works contains a great number of facts and quotations, useful and interesting in themselves, but the present writer feels that the authors have not only failed to prove their main contentions but have quite spoilt their book by trying, as George McCready Price and others in the U.S.A. have done, to attribute almost all of the geological ages to the Flood of Noah. The argument is thus reduced to absurdity.

The fourth suggested cause, this time proposed mainly for the Genesis Flood, is the advent of a great tide which rose, swept over a considerable region of the Earth, and died away. This is the main view put forward in the second of the books just mentioned, *The Biblical Flood and the Ice Epoch* by D. W. Patten. Once again this writer tends to follow up all sorts of by-ways including, for instance, his opinions on evolution and geology in general, and thus obscures the great value of his main thesis.

Two possible causes could be suggested for such a vast tide. Some have proposed a shift of the Earth's axis of rotation. We know that the Earth's magnetic poles have wandered very considerably, but the movement is slow, is still continuing, and would make no appreciable difference to tides. We know also that the so-called 'poles of cold' have shifted, and we have no certain ideas of the causes.[16] But the suggestion has been that the actual poles of rotation shifted at the time of the Flood. Again it is true that the Earth's axis 'leans over' at 23° 27' but this is certainly not unique among the planets. It is not usually affirmed that at the Flood the axis was tilted the whole 23° 27'; a shift of a single degree would throw an enormous tidal wave around the Earth. But no astronomer is prepared to say that any known force has ever shifted the Earth's axis of rotation in such a short time as the theory requires.

The other, and more plausible, suggestion which is really the main point argued in Patten's book, is the near approach of a minor planet or other such wandering object. We know in fact that some of the minor planets travelling in rather long elliptical orbits do come fairly near the Earth. Eros in 1900 was within 30 million miles and at its nearest approach it comes within 14 million miles. The little planet Apollo, discovered in 1932, came within 2 million miles of the Earth, passed inside the orbit of Venus and was lost track of when it went round the Sun. Two other very tiny planets, Hermes and Adonis, have also been observed coming very near to the Earth, so that Patten's contention cannot be lightly dismissed. His theory seems to require a minor planet much larger than Apollo or Hermes, and that the visitor came in very much closer than these bodies have done. It must be conceded that such bodies can come in close and even be captured by the Earth, since meteorites are almost certainly fragments from minor planets, and those that fell at Meteor Crater near Winslow in Arizona, and in Quebec must have weighed many millions of tons. They have still not ceased, for one weighing probably ten million tons fell in Siberia in 1908. If, according to Patten's theory, the wanderer came near but was not captured by the Earth, then its effect would not last for a year and its maximum tide-raising force would be much less. This theory—Patten gives many more details—is worthy of further investigation, and even if not correct as it stands, is the most reasonable that has been put forward recently. Patten also suggests that the wandering planet, like some comets, had a vast quantity of frozen gas particles with it, solids at temperatures like – 200 degrees Fahrenheit,[17] and that some of these, being captured by the Earth, caused the sudden intense freezing of the one-time fertile homes of the mammoths in Siberia and Alaska. This suggestion we shall meet again later. Any such 'seeding' of our atmosphere by solid, intensely cold particles as well as meteoric dust would obviously account for the deluge of rain observed by Noah and the vast snow-falls which covered Siberia. The theory certainly seems to hold well together.

But we cannot at present declare with any certainty which of the above factors operated in the time of the Flood. We have given a number of the possibilities that have been suggested merely for general interest. They are not intended as a proof that Noah's Flood did take place.

III

We come now to two questions which cannot easily be dealt with separately, the extent and dating of the Genesis Flood. When we come in Chapter 6 to consider the Ark and its possible contents we shall seek to show that despite the fact that in our modern terminology the account seems to refer to the entire planet as we now know it, the record could only have conveyed to the original writer the entire then-known world.[18] On the other hand, the tremendous and long-continued rainfall, the obvious violent upheavals of the ocean bed—the fountains of the Deep—and not merely swollen rivers, the direction of the drift of the Ark, and the fact that it settled in a mountainous region and not in a muddy plain near the Persian Gulf, and the very long time of settling of the waters, all make it perfectly clear that no local flood of the Tigris-Euphrates valley will ever fulfil the conditions required by the Genesis account. Again, to those who believe in the Biblical records, the promise of God that 'never again shall all flesh be cut off by the waters of a flood and never again shall there be a flood to destroy the earth'[19] would not have been kept if the Genesis Flood were just the drowning of the local regions of Mesopotamia and a few hundreds of people and animals. The great floods that formed the Zuider Zee, and the vast floods of the Yangtse and Yellow Rivers with their immense death-rolls have far exceeded the local floods of the Tigris or Euphrates. The Biblical account, especially when one considers later references, seems clearly to demand a flood of a completely different order.

So far as dating is concerned the Genesis record requires certain factors into which we shall look more carefully later. For the moment we need only observe the limits. The Flood occurred after man had been on the earth a long time and the population had begun to multiply. It occurred after the very early observations on the use of metal.[20] On the other hand it occurred long before Abraham went to Egypt and met one of the great Pharaohs. Within these limits of extent and time we can study the available data.

There are various methods of attempting to determine the dates of ancient events. For geological strata and for many fossils in them we may use analysis of uranium-bearing ores on the one hand and the fluorine content on the other. But the uranium method is of no use in dealing with archaeological remains where the times involved are only of the order of thousands and not millions of years,[21] and the fluorine methods are very far from exact.

The dates of the various phases of the Ice Age, formerly estimated by geological methods in thousands of years, have lately been estimated from an astronomical hypothesis of the causes of the Glacial Period which gives the various stages in hundreds of thousands of years. These dates are at present very popular with some scientists[22] and most newspapers and magazines, but are far from being certain, or universally accepted. These dates, however, do not worry us, for even those who accept them concede that the Ice Age virtually ended about 10,000 years ago, and on all counts the Flood has come since then.

For dates within such periods of some thousands of years the best known method of investigation is the radio-carbon method and although this has been often described it may be advisable to outline its principles again.

Our upper atmosphere is subjected to a continuous bombardment by cosmic rays which give rise to particles called neutrons which in turn collide with atoms of nitrogen in the higher regions of the air. As a result of these collisions atoms of radioactive carbon are formed and these are a little heavier than the ordinary ones whose atomic weight is 12 whereas the new ones are 14. These radioactive carbon atoms burn to carbon dioxide which then mixes with the air, the percentage being nearly constant all over the world. It follows that the carbon of all living things tends to contain the same percentage of carbon-14. The amount is extremely small, being estimated at 1.85×10^{-12}g. per g. of carbon-12. A dead object, however, ceases to draw any more carbon from the atmospheric carbon dioxide and hence its radioactivity dies steadily away. The rate of this 'dying away' follows a logarithmic law, and in fact half of it has gone in 5745 ± 50 years.[23] This time is known as the half-life period, and when another such period has elapsed half of what was still left will have died away . . . and so on. It is therefore only necessary to determine the percentage of carbon-14 remaining to be able to calculate the time since death. In practice there are several difficulties (which can be largely overcome) and the answer then depends on two assumptions. The chief difficulty is the fact that in any case the radioactivity is so very low especially after three or four half-lives and against a background of considerable outside interference which has to be guarded against by elaborate apparatus. The small standard deviation of 50 years on the half-life is of no real importance. The assumption that the carbon-14 content of the atmosphere has been constant over a very long period, say 30,000 years, is open to much wider question. Morris and Whitcomb have a long section in which they maintain that it has not, and a paper published in 1963 by Lingenfelter[24] also seems to indicate that the present rate of formation of carbon-14 is greater than it used to be, and indeed, by quite an important factor, which would make radio-carbon dates too high. Another assumption is that specimens have neither gained nor lost radio-carbon by physical or chemical means during the long periods that they have remained buried. But, in fact, it is known that specimens can lose their heavier isotopes of carbon preferentially to solutions containing carbon-12. This again will mean that the specimen will appear too old. If we consider briefly a number of radio-carbon results we shall be able to see exactly how reliable these datings are. A piece of charred bread from Pompeii, which was destroyed in A.D. 79, gave an age indication of 1850 ± 30 years, i.e. as near perfect as one could hope for. Wood from a boat of the Emperor Caligula (circa A.D. 40) gave results: 2010 ± 65, 2080 ± 150 and 1904 ± 95. These results are good but the first two are rather high for wood cut about 1920 years ago, and the range from 1904 to 2080 is rather wide. Wrappings from the pots of the Dead Sea Scrolls (about 1890 years old) gave figures of 1920 to 1965 years —again rather high. Columbia University obtained 1430 ± 150 years for wood from a Sequoia tree where the true age of 1377 ± 4 had been found by counting rings.

But for much older specimens the results become considerably less reliable. Material from the Grotto de la Garenne, said to be Magdalenian in date, gave ages of 9000, 11,000, 13,000 and 15,000 years B.P. (i.e. before present) on specimens which should have been contemporary. It is obvious that some very old specimens are showing dates that are considerably too high due either to loss of carbon-14, or to the fact that there was less carbon-14 in the atmosphere in those days.[25]

We have, then, a scientific 'tool' to use for age determinations which is very good for ages of two or three thousand years but which must be used with ever-increasing caution for very high dates. We shall quote these carbon-14 dates where relevant.

The other approach to the date of the Flood must be through the written records or archaeological remains of ancient nations, and although this chapter is mainly scientific it seems wisest to include such studies here.

The Biblical date of the Flood is not easy to determine with great exactness. The Hebrew text differs from the Septuagint Greek in the age at which each of the Patriarchs from Arphaxad to Nahor had his first son. The Greek also adds a second Cainan who is accepted in Luke's Gospel. If we assumed that the lists were complete the Bible would date the Deluge at about 2400 B.C. (Hebrew) or 3050 B.C. (Greek). But it is well known that in a number of cases the 'family trees' are not meant to be complete . . . only to give the true line of descent. Thus Ezra gives seventeen generations between himself and Aaron but if we compile a complete list there were over forty generations. It might well be that if we possessed more facts about the generations between Noah and Abraham[26] we should find a somewhat higher date for the Flood than 3000 B.C. Yet the vivid details of the story both in the Biblical and the Babylonian accounts seem to indicate caution in putting too many centuries between the actual Flood and the written records of it. Dates of the order of 4000 to 3000 B.C. would be within the reasonable framework of Genesis.

Before we consider the evidence from non-Biblical sources it is necessary to point out one constant source of error, or at least of danger, in dealing with periods of unknown duration. This is the curious tendency we have of allowing a few extra centuries or even thousands of years wherever we are in doubt.[27] It is partly because of this that many dates which were inflated to keep up with the 'archaeological Joneses' have had to be brought down considerably as knowledge has progressed. This fact we must bear in mind in dealing with many dates which are at present only conjectural.

It seems most reasonable to believe that the Flood took place at least some centuries before the rise of the great dynasties of the Middle East. The date of the First Dynasty of Egypt is interesting as illustrating the danger just referred to. Menes, the first king of that dynasty, was dated by Prof. Petrie in his History of Egypt (1903) as 4777 B.C. The British Museum Guide in 1920 gave 3300 B.C., and Prof. Anati, in *Palestine before the Hebrews* (1962), p. 320, gave 2900 B.C. *The Biblical Archaeologist* (Dec. 1967), p. 114 gives *c.* 2850 B.C. But even more curious is the fact that radio-carbon dates, which as we have said are frequently rather on the high side, give 2500 to 2100 B.C. for material from a First Dynasty tomb, and 2600 to 2200 B.C. for material from the tomb of King Zet who is believed to have lived before Menes. We can say, at least, that the dates of the First Dynasty have come down from about 4800 to 2800 B.C., i.e. a drop of 2000 years. Yet still archaeologists frequently ignore the warning about inflated dates.[28]

The early history of China is obscure, but the Chinese have records of a First Dynasty,[29] the Hia Dynasty, said to have been founded between 2200 and 1990 B.C. The Chinese have a 60-year calendar cycle and an eclipse is recorded as having taken place in the 58th year of the 32nd cycle.[30] This seems to have been an eclipse of the sun which took place on 22 February, 720 B.C. and if we add 31 complete cycles of 60 years, and another 58 years, we get 2638 B.C. as the commencement of this calendar. The significance of this is not certain. It has been suggested that the wandering descendants of Noah who finally settled in China had kept a reckoning of the years since the Flood.[31] One of the early kings said to have lived about 2400 B.C., reigned 102 years, and the earliest eclipse record is believed to date to 2137 B.C. Of course their whole calendar may have been invented many years after the Flood[32] but the figures are at least interesting and suggestive.

The Assyrian king lists carry us back to Puzur Assur I, the founder of a dynasty at about 2100 B.C. It is not clear who this monarch was. Puzur is merely his title, so that he might be the Asshur of Genesis 10. 22, where we read 'The children of Shem:

Elam and Asshur and Arphaxad and Lud and Aram'. Some assume that the text is here referring merely to tribal histories and is only saying that Asshur, i.e. the Assyrians, are a Semitic people. Others feel that, even if some generations have been omitted, in most cases individuals are being referred to, and that the text declares that a person called Asshur, whose descendants were Assyrians, was either the son, or at least a direct descendant, of Shem, son of Noah.[33] Even so we do not know for certain that the Puzur Assur of the records is the same person. It is quite true that the records give the names of some thirty persons before Puzur Assur, but no dates are given, and as the list includes the name of Adamu (Adam ?) it may easily be a vague list of names from before the Flood.

The list of kings and rulers of Babylon and other cities in Mesopotamia again leads to dates of the same order. The so-called First Dynasty of Babylon takes us back to famous monarchs like Hammurabi who was probably the sixth king of this group. His first year is given as 1792 B.C. by Macqueen[34] and 1728 B.C. by Pritchard. This would give a date of about 1894 B.C. as the highest for Sumu Abu the first king of the First Babylonian Dynasty. The dynasties of Akkad, Ur and Lagash go back still further, and may give dates like 2300 B.C. for Sargon of Akkad and even 2700 B.C. for Mes-an-ni-pad-da of Ur. The still earlier lists are curious, giving names of kings with reigns of 600, 800, and even 1500 years. In these early lists, too, mention is made of the Flood, and among the kings of the first dynasty of Erech is Gilgamesh, the hero of the epic in which the king goes to the garden of the gods and meets Ut-napishtim, the Babylonian Noah.[35] The Babylonians themselves would thus put the Flood somewhere back in the region of 3000 to 2700 B.C.

The written records of the past—Biblical and non-Biblical—would lead us to a date of the order of 3000 to 2500 B.C. for the rise of the great Empires and civilizations of the Middle East. They do not seem to suggest, or perhaps even to allow for, a very great stretch of time between the Flood and these developments, so that we may say the evidence seems on the whole to

favour a date for the Flood nearer 4000 to 3500 B.C. rather than
8000 B.C. when the Ice Age was ending.

Without at the moment seeking to narrow the range of dates
down any further, we may turn to the question of the extent of
the Genesis Flood. When discussing the capacity and contents
of the Ark on pages 81ff we shall see that the Biblical account
does not of itself demand a flood two or three miles deep covering
at one and the same time the entire surface of the earth as we
now know it, and compelling Noah to pack on board thousands
of species of animals and birds and insects. But while we reject,
on the one hand, a view so extreme, so equally should we beware
of the other extreme, which makes the Flood but a local affair of
the land of Sumer. The Bible seems to indicate very clearly that
the Deluge was in a class by itself; that it occurred once, and
once only, that nothing approaching it in scale will ever again
occur, and that the next (and doubtless astronomical) upheaval
will cause, not a Flood, but a fiery and final judgement to sweep
over the Earth's surface.

The present writer joins those who are convinced that the
Deluge covered a very large area. Various writers have argued
for a Flood extending from the Mediterranean regions, through
the Middle East and Siberia to Alaska and even beyond.[36] It may
be well to look again at the evidences for such a flood in those
and surrounding areas and within the dates 8/10,000 to 3/4000
B.C., remembering that, as different scholars follow different
time scales, what one man calls 5000 B.C. may be contemporary
with what another calls 7000 B.C.

A Flood of the size we have envisaged might reasonably be
expected to have important bearings on three aspects of the
ancient world, namely (1) climate and sea-level (2) man and (3)
animal and plant life. We shall investigate these points.

If the factors which caused the Flood also affected the Earth's
climate we should find evidences of such a change around the
dates in question. Professor L. Dudley Stamp in his *Man
and the Land* gives a chart,[37] the relevant part of which
reads:

B.C.	CLIMATE
1000	Sub-boreal
2000	Drier
3000	Atlantic
5000	Warm and wet
	BREAK
6000	Boreal
7000	Warm and dry

It will be observed that Prof. Stamp finds so great a change in climate in the period discussed that he inserts the word BREAK at about 6000 to 5000 B.C. on his time scale. It also appears from his book that by this date he means the time of very early Neolithic man. In discussing the considerable climatic changes of these times Prof. Charlesworth[38] also draws attention to the networks of dry river beds in the Sahara, and the dry wadis of Egypt, Arabia, and Somaliland together with creeks in the Atacama desert, remains of fish in the Sahara, and many dry waterfalls. He mentions that lakes in Africa once surrounded by human habitations are now beds of dry soda. Prof. Monkhouse[39] following studies by Dr. H. Godwin, speaks of the climate of East Anglia as changing from what he calls 'boreal' to 'Atlantic' around 5500 B.C. and he also places the breaching of the Straits of Dover at about the same time. Prof. Austin Miller[40] describes similar changes with dates of the same order and makes them coincident with the great Flandrian Transgression, at which time the Caspian and Aral seas were filled and the greater raised beaches from Greenland to Franz Joseph Land were formed. Since then great areas of the Earth have been steadily losing their supply of water. Palmyra, which once housed 100,000 inhabitants, has no longer a sufficient supply for a thousand. The once busy trade route from Persia to Petra has long been abandoned for lack of water. Evidently large areas which received a copious supply of water some thousands of years ago have not since then obtained sufficient to maintain their store.

The evidence points to a considerable climatic change at about the same period as the Flandrian Transgression, the breaking of the connection of Britain and France, the filling of the Caspian Sea and the beginning of the new human civilization or Neolithic Period.

It is to this second topic that we now turn. The Genesis account envisages the end of an ancient civilization and the rise of a completely new race, the descendants of Noah, who spread across the world from the Middle East.

Now the earlier race of men, Palaeolithic man, had spread abroad quite widely in the Earth. All the indications are that at some time, and by some means, this race died out. In our own land it seems that they were never numbered in more than hundreds,[41] but there came a time when they suddenly died out. The Neolithic peoples were a new race. To quote from a standard work on the period, 'Over the greater part of Europe there appears to be a great hiatus between the Palaeolithic and Neolithic cultures. Between the Magdalenian and the age of polished stone there certainly is a complete break. No two types of industry could be more sharply contrasted with one another.'[42] Prof. Charlesworth, speaking of this same sudden break, summarizes the evidence under three headings: (1) the extinction of certain Palaeolithic animals (2) the fact that Palaeolithic art died out and that Neolithic art did *not* develop from the earlier type and (3) that in caves Palaeolithic and Neolithic layers are sharply separated, often by a sterile layer, i.e. a layer free from human remains or culture.[43] Finally Prof. Carlton Coon in his *History of Man*[44] has a map showing how the Neolithic civilization spread from a centre around the Caspian-North Persian area, partly westwards towards Europe and North Africa, and partly eastwards to China and Japan. All this, of course, accords exactly with what we conclude from the Biblical account of the spread of mankind from Armenia, the region between the Black Sea and the Caspian, and we shall return to this topic with some additional evidence later.

The Biblical record that Noah was instructed to build an extremely large vessel, evidently for the preservation of a considerable number of animals, is again evidence that the account envisages a flood covering a very wide area, and one which would destroy animal life throughout that region. In this case we should expect to find evidences of the sudden death of large numbers of creatures within the period under review. And this again is exactly what we do find, and that to an amazing degree.

The first line of evidence concerns the annihilation of the woolly mammoth at the same time as Palaeolithic man disappeared from the Earth. The woolly mammoth was a huge beast about the size of the African elephant but with larger head and with great curved tusks, the longest recorded being 18 feet 7 inches[45] as compared with 11 feet 6 inches for the modern elephant. The Siberian mammoth had long woolly hair believed to have been originally red-brown. It had also a close underfur and beneath that, a skin very much like that of the modern elephant. Beneath this was a layer of three and a half inches of fat . . . not a great thickness considering the size of the beast. Some have asserted that the mammoth was specially adapted for life in Arctic conditions, but this has been firmly denied by others, who point out that the regions of Northern Siberia with anything like their present climate could not possibly have sustained herds of thousands of mammoths, each requiring something like two tons of food per week and thirty gallons of water a day,[46] especially when we remember that these embedded remains show that they were living alongside great herds of bison, sheep, horse and rhinoceros. Surely the evidence here is conclusive that a great change of climate has come over this vast area.

Mammoths, of course, existed on the Earth over a considerable period and many of them lived and died long before the Flood. But in the late Quaternary Period, when they were contemporary with man, they increased greatly in numbers, until suddenly they ceased to exist on the earth. There is no evidence of any mammoths surviving into Neolithic times.[47]

That they were for some time contemporary with early man is quite certain. There are numerous engravings and pictures made by Palaeolithic men showing the mammoth.[48] A human skull was found in 1865 near Colmar associated with the bones of a mammoth. At Predmost it is estimated that besides 14 to 20 human skeletons, 25,000 flint implements and hundreds of objects made from reindeer horn and mammoth ivory, the bones of some 800 mammoths were found. A strange oval grave was surrounded by a fence made of mammoth bones. It is interesting, too, to note that not only did the mammoths cease to exist in the area, but the very types of people living at Predmost have also disappeared.

As we have said, many mammoths lived and died long before the Flood, but this does not affect the fact that when they were becoming very numerous, they were suddenly and completely wiped out from the Earth and that at about the same time as the great break in the climate of Europe and Asia, dated by some as 6000 to 5000 B.C. Their bodies form the mammoth cemetery, one of the strangest facts on earth. Bones of the mammoth are found buried along two thousand miles of Arctic Siberian coast. Islands off the north coast are crowded with such remains. The island of Lyakhov, north of the Tungus Peninsula and no less than 600 miles *inside* the Arctic circle has an enormous number of mammoth bones and tusks. On the island of Kotelni, even further inside the Arctic regions, an explorer counted the remains of ten mammoths in a half-mile walk. The island was filled with bones of rhinoceros, bison, horse, ox, mammoth and sheep. Today there is practically no vegetation at all on the island! The islands of Bielkov and Stolbovni are likewise strewn with bones of ancient creatures. Mammoth bones have been dredged up from the Arctic Ocean, and storms have washed them up on the most northerly coasts. The explorer Wrangel found the same on Bear Island 500 miles further east. All this is true, not only of the northern coast and the lands now drowned under the Arctic Ocean, but of the banks of the great rivers, themselves flowing through hundreds of miles of tundra—the Ob, the Yenesei, the Lena, and the Indigirka and their tributaries. As these great rivers wear away their banks, so, from time to time, more and more mammoth bones are revealed. It has been said that there is not a river from the Don to the Chukchi Peninsula (which reaches to the Bering Strait) where mammoth bones have not been found. But even this does not end the story, for the vast cemetery continues across the Bering Strait, and masses of mammoth bones have been found in Alaska![49] As Sir Henry Howorth, who incidentally did not believe in the story of Noah and the ark, confessed, 'A very great cataclysm overwhelmed a large part of the earth's surface. A vast flood buried great numbers of animals under beds of loam and gravel and there was a sudden change in the climate in regions like Siberia and Alaska'.[50] The total number of mammoths in the Siberian 'cemetery' has been estimated at five million, and the total of other large mammals at a hundred million. The number buried in the Arctic Ocean and its islands and in Alaska is unknown.

A few mammoth carcasses have been found almost complete, preserved for centuries by the frozen soil until the advent of some slightly warmer series of summers, or the weathering away of cliffs and banks by rivers has exposed the remains. Some twenty or more have been observed before decomposition or wolves destroyed them. Sledge dogs have eaten pieces of the flesh, and the north Chinese have records of frozen mammoths whose flesh was edible.

Some of the mammoth bones must of course represent creatures who died at different periods, but the mysterious fact is that such a vast number seem to have died in one great catastrophe.[51] The radio-carbon dates are not very reliable as some were performed on hair and skin, giving dates like 30,000 B.P. (before present) while charcoal found near some sites, though not necessarily contemporary, gave 11,000 B.P. In addition to the fact that hair and skin are not really suitable materials for such tests, we have already seen that very high radio-carbon dates are in any case liable to wide errors especially if the specimen has been buried in such a way as to lose carbon-14 by exchange. Prof. Ramm (*Christian View of Science and Scripture*, p. 176, note 81) says that the *latest* of the mammoths is more than 30,000 years ago. In fact the latest seems to be one quoted as MC 215 and given by radio-carbon as 5610 B.P., i.e.

c

about 3600 B.C. which would fit the date of the Flood excellently.
We may well ask 'Why did they die out, as undoubtedly they did,
about five thousand or so years ago?' They did not die of old age.
The bones and bodies, both of mammoths and older animals,
show creatures of all ages apparently dying at the same time.
They did not lie down quietly and die of disease. Some died
standing up, frozen on the spot, others further north were
dashed to pieces. They did not die of hunger. Prof. Charlesworth
says 'they were not only fed, some were over-fed'. They had
plenty of food; food which they liked ... yet food which no
longer grows within hundreds of miles of their burial place.[52]
The food was still undigested in their stomachs ... one still had
food in its mouth. Examination shows that some died of sudden
shock with eyes and blood vessels violently distended. Experts
estimate that they were suddenly struck with extreme cold of
the order of –150° F. which froze these huge beasts before decomposition could set in. Finally, the plants which they were eating
were plants which normally grow in summer or autumn. Is it
just a coincidence that the Genesis Flood came in the autumn?[53]

But the mammoths are only the first part of the story. What
shall we say of the remains of rhinoceros, bison, and horses found
on Kotelni, where today neither shrub nor tree exists? What
shall we say of the jaguar, lynx, yak, sabre-toothed tiger and
even camel, frozen in the so-called 'muck' of Alaska? What shall
we say of the masses of piled smashed trees, sometimes over two
hundred feet high, found in New Siberia, hundreds of miles
inside the Arctic Circle, and not there alone, but in several other
regions? One cannot avoid some comparison with the great
meteorite of June 1908 which crashed into the Tunguska valley
in Siberia, destroying forests over a radius of twenty miles, and
producing earth tremors which were recorded throughout the
world. Although this meteorite probably weighed some millions
of tons it must have been small compared with those which long
before produced the great craters of Winslow in Arizona and the
still vaster one in Quebec province.[54] It must be admitted that
the whole evidence leans toward some such explanation as that

of Patten. He maintains that the Flood was caused by the near approach of some minor-planet-like body, which, as it swung close to the Earth, raised the great tide which Noah survived in the Ark. At the same time it flung across Siberia a trail of intensely frozen ice particles, such as we know exist in the solar system, at temperatures of the order of −150° F. to −200° F.[55]

But there is yet a third line of confirmatory evidence to be recounted. There are, in numerous places, large crevices or fissures in certain hills filled with unusual materials. This material consists mainly of sharp fragments of stone, often mixed with clay and gravel, and cemented together with compounds of calcium. Such a mixture is technically called breccia (pronounced bretsha or bretshia and derived from an Italian word for broken walls). In special cases which we are to consider, this breccia is impregnated with the bones of many different types of animals all of which lived after the Ice Age. The crevices or fissures, which may extend downwards, either vertically or sloping, for two or three hundred feet, are then known as ossiferous fissures, and the contents as ossiferous breccia.

In the fissures at Oreston a curious collection of 1587 teeth, 147 jaws, 250 vertebrae and 26 skulls of various animals was examined by Mr. Cottle.[56] The bones showed no signs of teeth marks or of wear by rolling in water. Bones were sharply broken, and there was not one single whole skeleton. At Santenay, near Châlons, in France, there is a hill which rises over a thousand feet above the surrounding valley of the Saone. In the hill itself there are two ordinary caves containing bones of animals, including those of many species which no longer live in France, such as the lion, elephant and rhinoceros. These caves had been the dens of carnivorous animals, but near the summit is a fissure containing yellow earth intermingled with broken bones of lions, horses, wolves, foxes, bears, badgers, oxen, deer and rhinoceros. These bones show no signs of having been gnawed. Prof. Gaudry, who examined them, concluded that this strange accumulation could be attributed neither to man nor to animals.[57] Similar ossiferous fissures containing bones of nearly the same types of animals as those at Santenay have been found at Gibraltar. Once again these bones are smashed but not water-worn or gnawed, and all types are completely intermingled. One of the most interesting collections of all is that found near Palermo in Sicily. Here the ossiferous breccia contains a vast number of hippopotamus bones,[58] from animals of all ages down to babies, together with a few deer, ox and elephant. All the bones are smashed and scattered, but not gnawed. But this time the breccia is found in a cave at the base of a kind of amphitheatre of hills surrounded by steep slopes from 2000 to 4000 feet high, and open only seawards. Evidently whatever creatures lived on this semi-circular plain were driven back to the base of the hills by rising water which then drowned them, smashing them on the beach and finally pouring the fragments together with rubble and red clay from the cliffs above into the cave.

Examples of similar fissures and collections of bones can be found at numerous other places including Corsica, Sardinia, Italy, the Balearic Islands, Malta, Yugoslavia, Corfu, Greece, Crete, Cyprus, Asia Minor, South Russia, and North Africa. Prof. Prestwich, who records the most complete account of them, and Dr. G. F. Wright, who reconsiders the evidence, both conclude that these fissures were filled with smashed bones during a relatively *short* period when the land was below the sea. The geological evidence is also clear that this period was at the end of the Palaeolithic era, and within the period of the destruction of the great herds of mammoths in Siberia.

A few very unsuccessful attempts have been made to avoid the obvious conclusions from all the above facts. Some have said that perhaps the animals may have fallen into the fissures. The evidence is completely against this. In such cases the skeletons would have been largely complete, whereas they are scattered and incomplete and hopelessly intermingled. Others have tried to argue that carnivorous animals may have dragged the bones to these fissures. But caves of carnivorous animals are well known and are completely different from these, and the bones are never gnawed. The fissures are not caves or anything like caves. They are splits in the earth . . . just such as might have occurred either under the stress of a passing 'moon' which was raising a great tide, or by the bending of vast areas of land as they were depressed and rose again after some brief upheaval such as that which seems to have taken place at the time of the Genesis Flood.

Finally it used to be argued, and Prof. Ramm has unfortunately repeated the idea (*Christian View of Science*, p. 166) that no such flood could have reached France, despite the evidence of Santenay, Dinant-sur-Meuse and other places, because, so it was alleged, the volcanoes of the Auvergne are Tertiary volcanoes and the ashes they have thrown up are still unmoved after millions of years.[59] Unfortunately for this argument there are old French records that the Auvergne volcanoes, far from dying out millions of years ago, underwent violent eruptions in the years A.D. 458–460![60]

It could of course be suggested that we are dealing with the evidences for a series rather than a single flood. It might just possibly be so, but even then it but proves that several great floods took place between the end of the Ice Age and the rise of the great dynasties.

But in fact there is no proof that we are dealing with a series. Rather does everything point to these happenings being contemporary. The evidence fits perfectly into a pattern of one single astronomical or geological event, which caused the flooding within a very *short* space of time, of a vast area stretching from Western Europe through the Middle East and Siberia to Alaska. And this is just what we should expect from the Biblical references to the Flood.

Our final studies in this scientific section must deal with the archaeological evidences from the ancient cities of Mesopotamia.

The story really commences with the excavations by Dr. H. R. Hall in 1919 of the little mound of al'Ubaid, four miles north of Ur. These yielded interesting remains of pottery and various

flint and obsidian tools of the Neolithic age. The al'Ubaid type
of pottery seems to have come from the East—possibly from
Elam. In 1929 (Sir) Leonard Woolley, having completed his
famous excavations of the Royal Cemetery at Ur—a cemetery
which was a little older than the First Dynasty—drove a shaft
down to virgin soil and in so doing discovered an eight foot
layer of clean, water-laid silt, with pottery of the al'Ubaid type
both above and below it. This, he and his wife both concluded
was laid down by the Genesis Flood. During the following
season Woolley sank a very much larger shaft 75 feet by 60 feet
and went down finally 64 feet. This shaft penetrated eight levels
of houses and then went through no less than eighteen feet of
pottery rubbish—evidence in fact of a pottery factory where
'wasters' had been thrown out. Some red and black painted
fragments were the same as those discovered at a site called
Jamdat Nasr, 150 miles north of Ur. Still lower in this 'kiln'
stratum the pottery became much plainer and belonged to the
Uruk (Erech or Warka) type, and a heavy potter's wheel was
found. Below this level came the hand-turned, painted al'Ubaid
type of pottery—just a thin layer—and then the so-called Flood
silt. A few graves from above penetrated down into this and in
one there was a copper spear-blade. A number of little terra-
cotta figurines were found. The flood silt here was eleven feet
thick, 'Absolutely uniform and clearly water-laid, subject to the
action of gentle currents and composed of material brought
down from the middle reaches of the Euphrates'.[61] Below it were
at least three levels of occupation and the pottery was again of the
richly decorated al'Ubaid type.

As we have said Woolley and his co-workers were convinced
that this 8–11 feet layer of silt was deposited by the Noachian
Flood and at first this view was almost universally accepted.
Other, though lesser, layers were found in several places, but
more careful examination of all the evidence led a number of
workers to question whether these belonged to the same period
and whether in fact any of them dated to the Deluge of Noah.
Woolley seems to have retained his conviction until his death

but he certainly believed that the flood which produced the deposit at Ur was merely a considerable local flood in the Tigris-Euphrates valley, the water being probably no more than 25 feet deep.[62]

It will be seen that the description of this deposit at Ur does not coincide with the period to which so much other evidence compels us to assign the Flood of Noah. The Ur deposit obviously comes well in the Neolithic age and certainly not at the break between the Palaeolithic and the Mesolithic. It must then, as almost all now concede, belong to a time many centuries later than the Deluge. But this at once gives us the clue to something which is nearly always overlooked in Woolley's description. If the silt layer belongs to a period 500 or 1000 years later than the Flood, then the evidence for the Flood lies deeper down. Woolley in fact did continue on down. In his own words, 'Below the silt came the level of human occupation—decayed mud brick, ashes and potsherds, in which we could distinguish three successive floor levels; here was the richly decorated al'Ubaid pottery in abundance, flints, clay figurines and flat rectangular bricks, and fragments of clay plaster, hardened by fire, which on one side were smooth, flat or convex, and on the other side bore the imprint of reed stems, the daub from the walls of the reed huts which were the normal houses of the pre-flood people. The first huts had been set up on the surface of a belt of mud which was clearly formed, for the most part, of decayed vegetable matter. In this layer of mud were potsherds (thicker at the bottom of the belt) all lying horizontally as if they had been thrown there and had sunk of their own weight through water into soft mud; below this again, three feet below modern sea level, there was stiff green clay pierced by sinuous brown stains which had been the roots of reeds; here all traces of human activity ceased and we were at the bottom of Mesopotamia'.[63]

Here then was the mud and decayed vegetation of an earlier flood. This flood had swept from some neighbouring but unknown site some pots which it had dropped. The flood had withdrawn, the land had risen slightly, the mud had hardened.

Men had come once again to build huts and a new civilization had grown up long before the eleven feet silt level.

Was this flood caused by the sinking of Mesopotamia and the rising of the level of the Persian Gulf, or was this the time of Noah's Flood—or are these only different ways of referring to the same catastrophe? At least one thing is certain: there is a layer of mud a dozen feet further down than the famous silt layer. Water had swept over the area long before Woolley's Flood, but still within the times when man could make pottery.

These observations need not in any way surprise us. We have already seen that there is considerable evidence for risings and sinkings of land in Europe, including the Genesis Flood as one of these, but extending right into Bronze Age times. The Middle East has been no exception and Mesopotamia has suffered several floods. It is in fact believed that the southern area is again sinking slightly.[64] Once this is granted all the evidence from Ur and other centres falls easily into place. At Kish there is a deposit of clay about a foot thick but above a cemetery which is itself above a layer of pottery of the Jamdat Nasr type. This clay must then be much later than the silt deposit of Ur which is well below the Jamdat Nasr Period. At Erech (Warka), too, there is a layer of nearly five feet of sterile mud (i.e. free from human remains) but it is also well above the Jamdat Nasr type of pottery. A similar layer of mixed clay and sand eighteen inches thick was found at Fara (ancient Shuruppak, legendary home of Ut-Napish-tim or Noah), but this too comes between the Jamdat Nasr type of pottery and the remains of the earliest dynasties.

The excavations of Prof. Mallowan at Nineveh again reveal a very interesting story. Here, at a depth of 27 feet from the surface the excavators found Jamdat Nasr ware. Very much farther down, at 51 feet, they found a layer of black mud with pebbles, and at 57–60 feet a consecutive series of thirteen layers of mud and river sand alternating. The excavators consider that this represents a 'well-defined pluvial period' and that it co-incided with an important climatic change. A copper pin was found at this level, being the earliest copper found. It would seem then that this deposit might be much nearer in time to the 8–11 feet silt at Ur, and in that case the evidence for Noah's Flood would be still deeper down.

Below the thirteen mud and sand layers at Nineveh was an earlier civilization called 'Nineveh 2', with charred wood, red and black painted pots and a thin layer of mud. Still lower (Nineveh 1) the pottery became plain, but at 81–84 feet there was again a layer of black mud. Below this was very hard red soil.

It looks then as if, after the Deluge, the region of Mesopotamia was but little above river-and-sea-level and for many centuries was liable to flooding, sometimes on a fairly large scale. The black mud at 81 feet down at Nineveh was either left by the subsiding waters of the Deluge or by the next inundation which swept across that region before it was inhabited. The artistic remains of Nineveh 2 and 3 are said to be somewhat like those of Aurignacian man, and thus we have evidence that the art of Mesopotamia soon after the Flood shows a resemblance to that of Western Europe just before.

The evidences from Ur, Kish, Warka, Fara and Nineveh show that this area has been subjected several times to floods, separated in time by centuries and probably all subsequent to the Genesis Flood, save possibly that which left the mud of the very lowest levels of Ur and Nineveh. These movements of the Middle East seem to have been the Earth's final undulations after the great Deluge.

We must now, in conclusion, look back briefly over the varied and curious facts which have been examined. Vast areas of the Earth have been drowned beneath the oceans in bygone days. The rise and fall of continents became by no means less or slower in what are termed 'Recent' times, i.e. since the end of the Ice Age. Rather did they then reach a maximum. Some time after the end of the Ice Age, and before the rise of the great dynasties, a great flood, caused either by the close approach of some heavenly body, or by the movement of the continents, or both, swept from the Atlantic, the Mediterranean, and the

Indian Oceans over much of Europe and Asia to Alaska and even beyond. During that period Palaeolithic man disappeared, the entire climate of Siberia was radically changed, herds of mammoths were completely eliminated, some being apparently almost instantaneously frozen to death by unprecedented cold, and the sabre-toothed tiger, the woolly rhinoceros and a hundred million other creatures perished. Herds of animals in Europe and Western Asia were trapped by rising water and many were dashed to pieces, their bones being swept into great cracks which had appeared in the earth. Lesser risings and fallings of certain local areas have continued, giving rise to raised beaches, shifting levels of fens in England, or various flood levels in Mesopotamia, but these are obviously small compared with the event which drowned a hundred million animals and exterminated an ancient race of men. That great oceanic tide, accompanied in the Middle East by torrential rain, and in Siberia by intensely frozen snow, capable of floating and indeed of driving a 10,000 ton wooden barge, probably from Mesopotamia to the regions of Ararat . . . that Flood which Genesis describes so minutely, was surely unique in history, and, by the promise of God, was not to be repeated—and in fact, never has been.

Is it possible that the next time some planet-like satellite sweeps close to the earth, or it may be fragments from it enter our atmosphere, that world which can never again be destroyed by a flood will be destroyed by fire? Is it possible, in fact, that the Creator has placed the history of civilized man between two great astronomical events, the former of which stands as the age-long warning of the second?

NOTES

1. L. J. Wills, *A Palaeographical Atlas*, plate xix. It is also perhaps worth noting that some of the rocks of the Caucasus, originally deposited in horizontal layers, are now folded through 180° owing to colossal upheavals in that area—an area not far from Ararat itself. Similarly, some rocks of North Africa have been tilted 45° *since* Palaeolithic times.
2. L. C. King, *The Morphology of the Earth*, pp. 506, 507, 516, 520, and 528. Lakes Van and Urmia, near to Ararat, 5600 feet and 4200 feet above sea level respectively, are both salt. On the southern shores of Lake Van are

two clearly defined 'raised beaches', one 1600 feet and the other 320 feet above the present level of the lake. The whole level has changed in *historical* times, and Pliny asserts that Lake Van was once connected with the Tigris. For other considerable earth-movements in this region, some in Recent times, see H. F. B. Lynch, *Armenia*, Vol. I. p. 442.

3. It may be noted here that Prof. Charlesworth attacks and rejects attempts to attribute all, or most, of the geological strata to the Flood, and he is thus sometimes quoted as disproving all geological evidence for the flood. This is, of course, an entirely wrong deduction from his writings, as the present quotations show. See J. K. Charlesworth, *The Quaternary Era*, Vol. 1. pp. 604–606.

4. L. Picard, *Structure and Evolution of Palestine. Bull. Geol. Dept. Hebrew University, Jerusalem*, 4. (1943), p. 158, believes that the Jordan came into existence at the *end* of the Pleistocene, and that the alluvium of the ez-Zor plain was actually formed in Neolithic times.

5. G. M. Lees and N. L. Falcon, *The Geographical History of the Mesopotamian Plains, Geographical Journal*, (1952), cxviii Part. 1. and cf. R. L. Raikes, *Iraq*, Vol. xxvii, Part. 1. (1966), p. 59.

6. A. Geikie, *Text-book of Geology*, pp. 279, 895.

7. J. Prestwich, *On Certain Phenomena belonging to the close of the last Geological Period*, pp. 5, 29, 45.

8. W. B. Wright, *The Quaternary Ice Age*, p. 412, says that the submergence registered by the Flandrian deposits will probably be found to be of almost world-wide extent.

9. A. Austin Miller, *Climatology*, pp. 299, 300.

10. In water-holes in the middle of the Sahara desert there are still living creatures, including crocodiles, identical with those found in Central Africa. C. B. M. Mc.Burney, *The Stone Age of Northern Africa*, p. 70.

    The Sahara was once forested and inhabited by elephants, giraffes and aquatic animals. *Geographical Magazine*, December, 1964. p. 603. P. O'Connell, *Science of Today*, p. 19, quotes Marcelin Boule, *Les Hommes Fossiles*, for the statement that Old Stone Age remains are widespread across the Sahara. He would date them 10,000–8000 B.C. There seems to have been no Mesolithic Period in North Africa.

11. Lt. Col. L. M. Davies, *J. Trans. Vict. Inst.* 1930.

12. Genesis 7. 11.

13. H. M. Morris and J. C. Whitcomb, *The Genesis Flood*, p. 121. These authors quote American meteorologists as estimating the total water-vapour content of the atmosphere above the United States as being sufficient to give a total of $\frac{3}{4}$ inch if spread over the whole land. They themselves, however, believe that the Flood was caused by the sudden condensation of a vast vapour canopy. The present writer feels that this theory would require much clearer scientific evidence than that provided by Morris and Whitcomb. The present mass of the oceans is estimated as 1.37×10^{18} metric tonnes, and the atmospheric water as 1.3×10^{13}. Thus the total rainfall could only add one part in 100,000 to the volume of the oceans, increasing the mean depth by 0.12 feet, i.e. about 1.4 inches.

14. M. E. L. Mallowan, *Noah's Flood Reconsidered, Iraq*, Vol. xxvi, Part. 2. (1964), p. 62.

15. R. L. Raikes, *The Physical Evidence of Noah's Flood, Iraq*, Vol. xxviii, Part 1. (1966), p. 52. Raikes refers also to evidence from Dar-i-Khazinah, and speaks of a single catastrophic flood in that area in about 3000 B.C.

16. Coal is mined in Spitzbergen and numerous other northern regions. Fuchs found coal in the Antarctic. See *The Crossing of Antartica*, pp. 106, 213.

17. The surface temperature of Saturn is believed to be below −150° C. and of Neptune, −165° C. (−265°F.). Some comets seem to have come from regions where the temperature was below −243ᵛ C.

18. This argument can be taken too far. Mr. Woodhouse Beales, *The*

Witness, (February, 1968), p. 69, wisely says, 'If we denude the Scriptures of their prophetic and sometimes "typical" meanings, and simply explore "what they meant to the men and women of their times", we shall reduce them to mere books of history, homily and hymnology and be the losers thereby'.

In my book, *Creation Revealed*, I have shown that a number of words used in Genesis 1 were carefully chosen by the Divine Revealer because they were capable of a wider meaning as man's knowledge of the universe increased.

19. Genesis, 9. 11. RSV.

20. Genesis, 6. 1.

21. The 'half-life' of uranium-238 is of the order of 4500 million years. Such a 'clock' can never be used to measure periods of the order of 10,000 years or less.

22. The Astronomical Theory has been popularized by the late Professor Zeuner, in his *Dating the Past*, but he himself admitted more than once that these dates were put forward merely as 'possible' and 'tentative'.

23. E. Hughes and W. Mann. *International Journal of Applied Radiation and Isotopes*, (1964), Vol. 15. p. 97.

24. R. E. Lingenfelter, *Review Geophysics*, (1963), 1, 35–55, has shown recently that over the last ten solar cycles the production rate of carbon-14 atoms has exceeded the decay rate in the ratio of 2.5 to 1.8 atoms per sq.cm. per second. This means that there is not a true radio-active equilibrium in the atmosphere. If such a variation had occurred over the whole of the time since the Ice Age it can be shown by calculation that a specimen 10,000 years old would give a radio-carbon age of 30,000 years. Against this it does seem certain that no such large-scale variation has continued during the past 2000 years, as the figures from Pompeii show. The question needs careful study and, as maintained in this and in other books, the higher figures given by radio-carbon should be regarded as tentative.

25. It is not safe to assume that pottery and charcoal found in the same site are necessarily contemporary . . . or if they are that the radio-carbon date is always the correct one. Charcoal found at Cuicuilco, Mexico, gave a radio-carbon date of 6715±90 years B.C. The associated pottery was reckoned to be 2300 to 2700 years old. F. Hole and R. Heizer, *Introduction to Prehistoric Archaeology*, p. 148.

26. Ussher gives the birth of Abraham as 1996 B.C., F. Clinton as 2130 B.C., and M. Anstey as about 2038 B.C.

27. J. H. Pratt, in his *Scripture and Science not at Variance*, pp. 176–185, reports the example of a Mr. Horner who discovered some pottery at a depth of 39 feet from the surface in deposits around Memphis, and some burnt bricks even lower down. From the rate of deposits he calculated that these should be more than 13,000 years old. But the pottery seems to have been Mohammedan, and the bricks were of Roman times.

The 'Anau' civilization of Transcaspia was, in 1920, dated firmly as about 10,000 B.C. It is now known to be no earlier than 4000 B.C. The Keilor Skull, formerly hailed as 150,000 years old is now estimated at no more than 5000.

28. There is some curious evidence from Egypt. Scattered in the desert regions are ancient tree stumps. Some of these grew in very peculiar circumstances. There exist in several places the beds of ancient wadis containing water-laid silt, at the bottom of which are remains of early man. Trees grew and died in this silt, and later inhabitants, who were still pre-dynastic, in digging tombs have cut through the roots of these trees. We have then evidence of the two races of early man, separated by water-laid silt, and both belonging to pre-dynastic times. C. B. M. McBurney, *The Stone Age of Northern Africa*, p. 239, allows about 1000 years from the arrival of the primitive hunter-peasants in Egypt, to the

establishment of the first dynasty. Even this may be, as we have seen, too generous an allowance.
29. Larousse, *Encyclopaedia of Ancient and Mediaeval History*, p. 54.
30. S. A. Mitchell, *Eclipses of the Sun*, (1924), p. 7.
31. In China there is practically no evidence of a Mesolithic Period. The Palaeolithic ends abruptly and is followed by the Neolithic. *Encyclopaedia Britannica*, (1965), Vol. 5. p. 571. But see W. Ehrich, *Chronologies in Old World Archaeology*, pp. 507–518.
32. In India the present era or age called Kali-yuga, is said to have commenced in 3102 B.C. A. L. Basham, *The Wonder that was India*, p. 321.
33. Semitic names are found in early Assyrian lists.
34. J. G. Macqueen, *Babylon*, Appendix II., L. Woolley, *Excavations at Ur*, p. 253, J. B. Pritchard, *Ancient Near East*, p. 138.
35. See Chapter 2
36. P. O'Connell, for example ,in *Science of Today*, includes the regions mentioned and adds India, China, and North America east of the Rocky Mountains.
37. L. D. Stamp, *Man and the Land*, p.3.
38. J. K. Charlesworth, *The Quaternary Era*, p. 1112.
39. F. J. Monkhouse, *The Principles of Physical Geography*, p. 213.
40. A. Austin Miller, *Climatology*, pp. 299, 300.
41. C. and J. Hawkes, *Prehistoric Britain*, p. 31.
42. W. B. Wright, *The Quaternary Ice Age*, p. 269.
43. J. K. Charlesworth, *The Quaternary Era*, p. 870.
44. C. S. Coon, *History of Man*, p. 126.
45. The left one of a pair from a skull in a cliff near the Kolyma River. The tusk, which weighed 185 lb. is in the Leningrad Museum.
46. There are of course plenty of trees in parts of Siberia, but these get fewer and fewer towards the north . . . the vast tundra, most of which is permanently frozen. Only for a few months will the top of the soil thaw and produce moss and lichens. The strange fact is that almost all the mammoth remains are in the extreme north. Professor Charlesworth says that only two mammoths in Siberia were found south of the Arctic circle.
47. Bernard Heuvelman in *On the track of Unknown Animals*, Ch. 15, tells the story of Cossacks in the sixteenth century seeing hairy elephants and also the tale of a wandering traveller who was supposed to have found the lair of a herd of mammoths, but there is no real evidence to support these tales.
48. Max Raphael, *Prehistoric Cave Paintings*, (quoted from *Science and Religion*, Vol. 1. No. 2. (1948), p. 62). In the long cave at Combarelles fourteen mammoths are pictured on the walls in red and black. At Font de Gaume, not far away, a whole herd of mammoths is depicted as well as a representation of the woolly rhinoceros. These pictures are attributed to the Magdalenian age.
49. Mastodon remains have been found in parts of Bolivia far too high and cold, and with insufficient vegetation, for such massive creatures to have lived at such a height. Some are buried in water-laid gravel. I am very grateful to a missionary friend, Mr. R. B. Randall, who has spent many years in Bolivia, for information concerning these and other remains which strongly suggest that the Andes have risen to their present height since the extinction of the mastodon in that area, i.e. in geologically very recent times.
50. Sir Henry Howorth, F.S.A., M.R.A.S., *The Mammoth and the Flood*.
51. See I. T. Sanderson, *The Dynasty of Abu*, Ch. 4, for an interesting account of the 'collapse of their Empire'. He discusses various theories which have been put forward to explain away the extinction of the mammoths, but admits that they all fail.
52. J. K. Charlesworth, *The Quaternary Era*, pp. 648, 649.
53. See Chapter 7.

54. It is interesting to note that the meteorites which have collided with the Earth, although immensely old themselves, have fallen on to our planet in geologically recent times. Palaeolithic men seem to have collected glassy meteorites but no nickel-iron ones. The *Encyclopaedia Britannica*, Vol. 15. pp. 275, 276 (1966) believes that the number of meteorites falling in the centuries before Christ was higher than it is today. In early historical times men regarded iron as the metal which fell from the sky. The meteorite which fell near Winslow in Arizona made a hole 1500 yards across and 600 feet deep. It flung out some masses of rock weighing up to 7000 tons and is estimated to have hurled out altogether 400 million tons of rock. The pressure of the impact exceeded 1,000,000 lb. per square inch turning silica into new forms known as coesite and stishovite. The still vaster crater 15 miles across at Ries Kessell in Bavaria was also made by a meteorite whose size must have been enormous. Coesite and stishovite are found at Ries Kessel and other meteorite craters. The moon has many craters and J. O'Keefe in the very recent treatise on Space Science says: 'The presence of large asteroids such as Eros in orbits which approach the earth, makes it reasonably certain that impacts of a very large size occur both on the earth and on the moon with fair frequency' p. 641.

55. If, as is quite possible, the intensely frozen water from space was accompanied by solid ammonia, or other such gases, we have an additional explanation for the very sudden deaths of mammoths while eating their food.

56. G. F. Wright, *Scientific Confirmations*, p. 257.

57. J. Prestwich, *Phenomena of the Last Glacial Period*, p. 50.

58. One estimate gives the number of hippopotami as 2000.

59. See, for example, Smith's *Dictionary of the Bible*, Article 'Noah'.

60. J. H. Pratt, *Scripture and Science*, p. 203.

61. L. Woolley, *Excavations at Ur*, p. 31.

62. L. Woolley, *Excavations at Ur*, pp. 35, 36. J. Prestwich, *Phenomena*, p. 75, mentions that in modern times the Tigris has risen in flood 22 feet and on one occasion left a 6 feet deposit.

63. L. Woolley, *Excavations at Ur*, p. 31.

64. Lees and Falcon, *J. Royal Geographical Society*, (1952). An Egyptian Government research vessel before the 1939 war discovered ten submarine hill ranges in the Gulf of Aden, and further east, below the Arabian Sea, two mountain chains and a raised plateau. There was also a deep river valley. There is evidence, mentioned by H. W. Saggs, *The Greatness that was Babylon*, p. 16, that aerial photography has shown the remains of an ancient civilization under the north end of the Persian Gulf.

CHAPTER 2

BABYLONIAN AND OTHER EARLY ACCOUNTS
OF THE FLOOD

WE come now to enquire what evidences of a great deluge are to be found lingering in the racial memory of mankind. If, as archaeology affirms,[1] an ancient race almost entirely perished and a new people spread across the world, or if, in other words, as the Bible affirms, the present races of mankind are descended from one family who alone survived the Deluge, then these descendants, as they spread across the world, will have carried the story with them. It will follow inevitably that as races migrated further and further, the story itself will have grown more and more confused and debased and we must first ask what factors thus operate during the transmission of an ancient story. These seem to include the following:

A. Factors tending to modify the truth of a story.
  1. With the passing of time some details become forgotten and others are invented to take their place.
  2. Details are changed to fit the local circumstances of the peoples to whom the story is being told. Mediaeval artists frequently depict Old Testament characters dressed in Italian robes. Even in recent times Israelites were often pictured as going through the wilderness with neat little army bell tents.
  3. Local circumstances and happenings get woven into the original story. Here we must guard against the stories of local floods which may have become added to the general account.

37

4. There has always been a tendency to bring ancient
   heroes and gods into primitive stories.

B. Factors tending to stabilize the transmission of a true
   account.
   1. The invention of writing. This is especially valuable if
      the original account is early committed to writing and
      if the scribes or translators are careful in their work.
   2. The excellent memories of peoples who rely less on
      written accounts. Numerous cases have been quoted by
      missionaries of people who could recite whole gospels
      and books of the Bible by heart and with practically no
      mistake. Children and primitive peoples do not like a
      well-known story to be altered by a story-teller.
   3. Individuals, kings and races who carefully preserved
      their own genealogy generally tended to preserve
      records of their ancestors. Hence the many ancient
      records of the Babylonians and Assyrians and, in the
      case of the Deluge, the account of the Jews who claim a
      known and recorded descent from Shem, son of Noah.

It is now widely recognized that the operation of the above two
sets of influences means that almost all legends and myths have
an element of historical truth behind them. One or two illustrations of this may be given. At Cuerdale, in Lancashire, there had
long been a tradition of buried treasure. In 1840 a hoard of silver
coins, ornaments and ingots, probably of Danish origin, was
unearthed on the spot. Near Mold in Wales tradition alleged
that at times a soldier in golden armour walked around the
barrow or mound at Bryn-yr-Ellylon. Excavators in 1832 found
that the barrow contained the bones of a man wearing a bronze
and gold corselet of the Roman period.

In Somerset legend had long maintained that the gates of
King Arthur's castle were in a spot near Cadbury although the
area had been ploughed for centuries. It was found ultimately
that the spot covered the original entrance to an ancient British
stronghold. It may even be that some ancient custom lies behind

the legend of the 'Golden Fleece'.² While some early accounts speak merely of a large fleece, possibly purple, all traditions from the time of Hesiod onwards call it the 'Golden Fleece'. Strabo recognized that this probably reflected the fact that ancient workers used to extract gold particles from auriferous sands by washing them down sheep skins. In fact this differs little from the modern method still occasionally used of collecting gold particles on rough blankets.³

We should expect, then, that the many Flood stories will each contain some elements of truth—though in varying proportions. Those factors or aspects which are common to the largest number are likely to be the most primitive and probably the nearest to the truth.

We shall seek to follow these Flood stories in outline from their original centre to the ends of the earth. Both archaeology and the Bible put the home of the new civilization in the regions around Armenia—the Caucasus and Caspian. From this centre the new race spread through Persia, to Assyria, Akkad and Sumer, and here we shall find some of the oldest Flood stories. But we shall follow others of the family through Central Asia, to China and India and Indonesia; to Ceylon, Burma, Australasia and Polynesia; across the Bering Strait through the lands of the Eskimos and the North American Indians, to Peru and Chile, and the far south. Yet others of the newly expanding race brought the story with them into Greece and Europe while others carried it through Egypt deep into Africa.

Among these non-Biblical accounts of the Flood some of the most ancient are those circulated in the regions now called Mesopotamia. Here there were several variations of the story and, as time went on, the account was merged into the legends which grew up around their king, Gilgamesh. We have no direct access to the originals of the story but we have (a) the accounts given of it by Berossus (b) fragments of very early tablets and, of course, (c) the later Gilgamesh story in considerable detail.

Berossus was a Babylonian priest of the god Bel, born in the

D

time of Alexander the Great. He had access to records which
have long since perished and some of these he translated into
Greek probably around 260–250 B.C. His historical work has
been lost but fragments of it have been preserved in other writers,
including Josephus and Eusebius.[4] His account of the Flood as
transmitted through Polyhister, Eusebius and Syncellus is as
follows:

'After the death of Ardatos, his son Xisuthros reigned eighteen
sars (i.e. 18 × 3600 years). In his time a great Flood took place
the history of which is thus described. Kronos appeared to him
in a vision and told him that on the fifteenth day of Dasios[5] there
would be a Flood by which mankind would be destroyed.
Kronos commanded Xisuthros to write a history of the beginning, procedure and end of all things[6] and to bury it at Sippar.
Then he must build a boat and enter it with his friends and
relations, and put on board provisions, together with birds and
quadrupeds . . . He obeyed and built a boat five stadia long and
two stadia wide,[7] and when all was ready he embarked his wife
and children and friends. After the Flood had come and abated
Xisuthros sent out birds from the vessel. These, however,
having found neither food nor resting-place came back to the
ship. After an interval of some days he sent them out again but
they returned with their feet soiled with mud. When he let them
go a third time they did not return to the ship. Xisuthros knew,
therefore, that land had reappeared, and when he had removed a
part of the ship's side he saw that they were grounded on the
side of some mountain. With his wife, daughter and the pilot he
quitted the ship and having bowed to the earth erected an altar
and offered sacrifices. The group thereupon disappeared and
those who had remained in the ship landed and called for
Xisuthros. He did not appear but a voice from heaven told them
to reverence the gods among whom Xisuthros had gone to dwell.
They were bidden to return to Babylon and told to recover the
writings from Sippar and share them with men. The place in
which they then were was Armenia. Hearing this they went to
Babylonia. Of the ship, which had there rested, there still remains

a portion in the mountains of the Gordyaeans in Armenia, and men scrape off asphalt and use it to ward off evil. Those who came to Babylonia dug up the writings at Sippar and founded many cities and shrines and repeopled Babylonia.'[8]

The date of this variation of the story is unknown. The last paragraph about men scraping asphalt from the ark is plainly a later comment. There is no reference to Gilgamesh or his contemporaries and no evidence that either Berossus or his transcribers made any substantial alteration in the story before them. There are several curious and interesting features which will be commented on later.

We now have evidence that neither Berossus nor his transcribers invented the account, for several very ancient cuneiform records have been found which throw light on the persons mentioned. Berossus calls Xisuthros the son of Ardates or Otartes. The prisms acquired by the English collector, Weld-Blundell[9] (W. B. 444 and 62) state that Ubar-Tutu, or Ubara-Tutu, was the father of Su-kur-lam who was the father of Ziusudra. Thus the name of Ziusudra's grandfather has been modified, in the course of time and copying and translating into Greek, to Ar-Dutu or O-Tutu, while the name Ziusudra has changed but little to Xisuthru. The later Gilgamesh legend still gives Ut-napishtim (i.e. Ziusudra or Noah) as the 'son' of Ubara-tutu.[10]

The story of the Flood seems to have been so well known that it became one of the popular 'books' in the ancient cuneiform libraries, and fragments of a number of slightly differing texts are known. One broken fragment from Sumeria[11] speaks of the Flood sweeping over the land and 'tossing the huge boat about'. It tells how 'Ziusudra the king, the Preserver of the seed of mankind . . . opened a window of the huge boat'.[12] Several similar fragments were referred to by Prof. Kramer[13] and in two of these we are told that the Flood 'wiped out everything'. Yet another ancient fragment[14] tells how the god Ea commanded Atra-khasis to 'enter the ship, close its door, bring in grain, livestock and possessions, as well as wife, kinsfolk and craftsmen'.

The god promised to send him 'beasts of the field, as many as eat grass'. He was also told to 'mark out the plan of the boat on the earth'. A fragment dated by the scribe as 28th Shabatu of the year in which King Ammizadugga built the city Dur-Ammizadugga[15] again refers to a great Flood, a ship with 'bolts', and to Atra-khasis[16] as the equivalent of Noah.

A small fragment discovered at Nippur[17] and undoubtedly of very early date speaks of a flood 'sweeping away all mankind at once' and of someone building a 'great ship . . . with a strong roof' in which vessel 'beasts of the field, the birds of heaven and . . . the family' were saved.

By far the most complete account of the Flood in non-Biblical literature is that given in the Gilgamesh Epic, in which the story-tellers supposed that the king, Gilgamesh,[18] after a long voyage came to Ut-napishtim 'the Faraway'[19] and asked him about the Flood. The account, which is given in the eleventh of the twelve tablets found in the library of Ashur-bani-pal, tells how Ut-napishtim was commanded by the god Ea[20] to build a ship on board of which he was to take the 'seed of all living things'. Ut-napishtim obeyed this command and laid out the plan of the ship on the ground, covering an area of 120 by 120 cubits.[21] He says that he put six decks within, dividing the ship into seven parts and the floor plan into nine parts. This latter reference is probably to cross-walls or bulk-heads giving strength to the ship and forming the 'rooms' of Genesis 6. 14. He says the he hammered water-plugs[22] into it and then poured molten bitumen and pitch over the inside together with oil to help in making it water-tight.[23] It seems that children or young people were employed to carry bitumen while 'strong-ones', presumably adults, brought the other material. When the ship was built a feast was held—as on a New Year's day—and the ship was launched. Ut-napishtim says that he then loaded the boat with silver and gold, with his family and kinsfolk, with cattle and beasts of the field including wild creatures, and also with the craftsmen. Finally Ut-napishtim and the master boatman, Puzur-Amurri, went aboard and fastened up the door. Then came the great Deluge which lasted seven days and terrified the gods who 'cowered like dogs' and 'sat down and wept'. The ship at last came to rest on Mount Nisir and after it had been held fast there for a week Ut-napishtim released a dove which, however, came back, as did also a swallow. Later he sent out a raven which did not return. Ut-napishtim offered a sacrifice on the mountain and the god Enlil (Bel), who had at first been angry that anyone should escape the Flood, made Ut-napishtim and his wife into celestial beings. Gilgamesh seems to have fallen asleep at this point and Ut-napishtim told his wife to 'mark on the wall the days he sleeps' . . . a clue perhaps to the way early man kept his calendar. Gilgamesh awoke after seven days and the remainder of the story is not relevant to the Flood.

Such, then, is the Babylonian account of the Deluge. It is unquestionably, in its original form, a very ancient and in some ways a very valuable record. There has been much argument in the past concerning its relation to the Biblical account; early followers of the German Higher Critical School rushed to the conclusion that the Hebrew story is 'plainly derived from the Babylonian'. Even so learned a scholar as Dr. J. Skinner in the *International Critical Commentary on Genesis* commences by saying[24] 'The dependence of the Biblical narrative on this ancient Babylonian legend hardly requires detailed proof', but by the time he has surveyed a little of the evidence he confesses, 'Here we have additional indication that the story was not drawn directly from a Babylonian source but was taken from the lips of common people'.[25] Finally he climbs down to: 'There is some subtle affinity between the two streams of tradition' . . . a rather pathetic understatement which means that the evidence is so overwhelming as to force him against his own Higher Critical upbringing, to admit that the Biblical and Babylonian accounts are separate though related streams. This is absolutely true and herein lies the strength of both. They are independent of each other yet alike in so many points as to convince the honest reader that they are both very ancient records of a real historical event. The Babylonian account is at present almost the only one which we possess which can be used to throw a little additional light on some of the details mentioned in the Biblical story and we shall in fact later so use it.

It is now necessary to survey some of the hundreds of Flood stories extant throughout the world, not with the object of gaining more information about the Deluge itself, for they afford little help in such a study, but rather to trace the migrations of the human race from that common centre around Armenia to the ends of the Earth.

Looking at the region of Armenia itself we have some geographical names remaining there which are plainly connected with the Bible story. Whether these names were in fact given to the places by the new inhabitants soon after the Flood, or some perhaps centuries later by mere tradition we have now no means of discovering; all we can do is to record the facts. Josephus[26] quotes Nicolaus of Damascus as saying that in Armenia there is a mountain called Baris where report says the Ark rested. Epiphanius says[27] that among the Gordyean hills of Armenia one peak, higher than the others, had the name Lubar which, he says, meant Descending Place. The traveller William de Rubruquis about A.D. 1253 says that in Armenia there was a little town called Nachuan near mountains called Masis and beyond these yet another place called Cemainum which he says means 'eight' . . . in memory of the eight persons saved in the Ark. The name Tabriz may be a corruption of Ta Baris—possibly 'mountain of the ship'.[28] *The Times* Atlas records a small town of NAHEIVAN some 40 miles S.W. of Ararat and a district called NAKHICHEVAN some 80–100 miles S.E. of the range. Thus it would seem that we still have in Armenia recollections of the name of Noah and of a ship, bearing eight people, resting on a mountain.

Moving now into the other regions of Asia Minor we find, first, that the Flood story was known to the ancient races of the Hurrians[29] and the Hittites although, so far, only fragments of the accounts have been discovered.[30] The Syrian people, too, had a Flood story the outline of which is preserved in Lucian's writings[31] in which he asserts that because of human wickedness the gods sent a deluge which was provided partly by torrential rain and partly by waters coming from the earth. From this deluge Deucalion and his family alone were saved in an ark which also housed horses, lions, snakes and other creatures all of which became tame. The second generation of the human race sprang from this Deucalion. Clinton and others believe that Lucian had met the Genesis account but others have denied this and the writer himself claims to have derived the account from the Greeks and says that it was a very ancient tradition.

The other Syrian record comes from Nicolaus of Damascus[32] who, in his ninety-sixth book says: 'There is a great mountain in Armenia over Minyas, called Baris, upon which it is reported that many who fled at the time of the Deluge were saved; and that one who was carried in an ark came on shore on the top of it; and that the remains of the timber were a great while preserved. This might be the man about whom Moses, the legislator of the Jews wrote'. The last sentence shows clearly that Nicolaus had heard of the Mosaic account but the story which he recounts is independent of the Bible because it allows that some folk other than those in the Ark were saved.

Keeping still to the Middle East we find traditions of the Flood in Phrygia. A coin or medal struck at Apamea shows a square chest floating on water. A man and a woman are advancing out of it while two people remain in it and above flutters a dove bearing an olive leaf. Another bird is perched on the ark and on the front of the chest are the Greek letters NOE. Several copies of this medal have been found. Some think that once again it shows Jewish influence and this may be so. Strabo does, however, mention that the Phrygian Apamea had the curious name κιβωτος (i.e. box, chest or coffer). There is also a Phrygian story of a king Nannakos or Annakos (= Enoch) in Iconium who reached an age of more than 300 years, foretold the Flood and wept and prayed for his people.[33]

The Phoenicians—an extremely ancient race—also had recollections of the Flood.[34] Bronze models of ships of Phoenician production, showing various kinds of animals standing in them, going back to the seventh century B.C. have been found in Italy and in Sicily. The Phoenicians also believed that Sydyk and his seven sons (making eight persons) were the builders of the first ship.[35] Josephus records that the Flood is mentioned by Hieronymus the Egyptian in his work on Phoenician Antiquities.[36]

NOTES

1. See above, p. 20.
2. W. Smith, *Dictionary of Greek and Roman Biography*, Vol. 1. Article Argonautae.
3. Strabo XI. 2. 19, Appian, *Bellum Mithridaticum*, 103. C. Singer, *A History of Technology*, Vol. 1. p. 581. J. R. Partington, *Origins and Development of Applied Chemistry*, p. 377 refers to gold mines in Armenia and among the Suani in Colchis and adds, 'The legend of the golden fleece probably represents the collection of gold dust in greasy sheepskins in the coast of torrents of Colchis, and the process survived in this region within living memory'.
4. Extracts were made by the Greek Historian Alexander Cornelius (Polyhistor) in the first century B.C. These were used by Eusebius of Caesarea but are known only through the transcripts of George Syncellus. There is an Armenian version which makes it possible to check the Greek text. The translation here given is based partly on Cory, *Ancient Fragments*, and partly on R. W. Rogers, *Parallels to the Old Testament*.
5. Dasios was the eighth Macedonian month and corresponded approximately to June. H. F. Clinton, *Fasti Hellenici*, Vol. III, pp. 349, 358.
6. This, for what it is worth, implies a belief that the art of writing was known to Noah.
7. The Biblical ratio of 6:1 is far superior. See below, p. 93.
8. Syncellus, 53–56. Seneca, Nat. Qu. 3.29 is said to have attributed to Berossus the belief that when the stars (i.e. planets) are in line in Capricorn there will be a great flood.
9. For a photograph of this Sumerian prism which gives the names of ten kings who ruled before the Flood, and adds 'then the Flood swept over the earth. After the Flood swept over, kingship again descended from heaven', see D. J. Wiseman, *Illustrations from Biblical Archaeology*, (1963), p. 8. Prof. Wiseman adds that there is actually a line drawn across the text to separate the postdiluvian events from those occurring before the Flood.
10. If this list could be relied upon we should have the following equations:

Ubara-tutu	=	Methuselah
Su-kur-*lam*	=	Lamech
Ziusudra	=	Noah

11. S. N. Kramer, *History begins at Sumer*, p. 200.
12. It also speaks of the 'hero' Utu bringing his rays into the boat. If this is the Sun-God we have another to add to the many clues that the Babylonian gods are derived from the 'heroes' or 'mighty men of renown' of Genesis 6 and the times of the Flood.
13. *The Times*, November 14 1964.
14. R. W. Rogers, *Cuneiform Parallels*. p. 104.
15. Ibid., pp. 105–107. There are Old Testament parallels for dating by the building of cities. Ammizadugga was a king of the first Dynasty of Babylon.

16. Atra-Khasis is usually taken to mean 'very wise'. A. R. Millard, in his excellent Tyndale Biblical Archaeology lecture, 1966, entitled *A New Babylonian 'Genesis' Story*, considers that it might be interpreted as 'exceedingly devout' which, of course, is even closer to the Biblical description of Noah as perfect (upright) and righteous.

17. R. W. Rogers, ibid. p. 108.

18. Gilgamesh was a king of Erech (Uruk), contemporary with the very early kings of Ur and Kish.

19. M. F. Unger, *Bible Dictionary*, (1957), gives Utnapishtim as 'Day of Life'. *The Encyclopaedia Britannica*, 9. 455 gives 'Uta is my life'.

20. The god Kronos of Berossus.

21. He says the ship was a cube, 120 cubits high as well as square. This, of course, would be absurd. The Ark in Genesis was 300 cubits long by 50 broad giving an area of 15,000 square cubits against Ut-napishtim's 120×120 i.e. 14,400 square cubits.

22. So Pritchard; Rogers has water-tanks and E. Wallis Budge (British Museum booklet, *The Babylonian Story of the Deluge*), has 'water-bolts'. They would seem to be the same as the 'bolts' of the fragment dated in the reign of Ammi-zadugga. See also the section on the construction of Ark, p. 91.

23. Pritchard gives six sar of bitumen, three sar of asphalt or pitch and three sar of oil and says that a sar (seah) as a measure might be 8000 gallons. See pp. 96ff for discussion of bitumen. The kind of oil is not specified.

24. *Op. cit.*, p. 177.

25. *Op. cit.*, p. 178.

26. Josephus, *Antiquities* 1. 3. 5. See also p. 114.

27. Epiphanius, *Adv. Haer.* Bk. 1.

28. G. S. Faber, *Horae Mosaicae.* p. 122.

29. O. R. Gurney, *The Hittites*, p. 123.

30. J. B. Pritchard. *The Ancient Near East*, p. 40. The hero in the Hittite version is named Na-ah mu-u-li-el.

31. Lucian was a Syrian believed to have been born at Samosata but he wrote in Greek. He alludes to the Flood in his work on Timon and in a Treatise on Dancing. The work *De Syria Dea* (*On the Syrian goddess*) which also refers to the Flood is probably by some other writer though attributed by some authorities in both ancient and modern times to Lucian. (See T. H. Horne, *Introduction to the Scriptures*, (1869 Edn.) Vol. 1. p. 157, and Smith, *Dictionary of Greek and Roman Biography*, art. Lucianus). The Syrian goddess, Derketo or Atargatis, was in some ways identical with the fish goddess. She was the wife of Hadad the Storm god. It is also worth noting that the Syrians worshipped the dove.

32. Josephus, *Antiquities* 1. 3. 6.

33. W. Smith, *Dictionary of Bible*, Art Noah. See also Suidas, sub. Annakos.

34. J. Skinner, *Genesis*, p. 180.

35. Eusebius, *Preparation for the Gospel*, 1. 10. Quoted from G. S. Faber *Horae Mosaicae.* p. 129.

36. Josephus, *Antiquities* 1. 3. 6.

CHAPTER 3

WORLD-WIDE RECORDS

MOVING now to a wider sphere we find that a variety of Flood stories persisted in Persia. Orthodox Persians believed that a widespread flood came upon the earth, some saying that it was universal, some that it extended only to a mountain between Assyria and Persia. Some alleged that the Flood came from the oven of an old woman named Zula-Cupha and this curious tradition still survives in the Koran.[1] George Sale, however, in his translation of the Koran mentions that the word rendered 'oven' also means the place of springing water, and as the Rabbis say that the water of the Deluge was hot, or as the Koran has it 'boiled over', it is probable that the Flood story has at some time become associated with hot springs. Further Cupha was probably a place. Yet another Persian story[2] has a general Deluge sent to wash away the world's sin, and a vessel known as the Arg of the Magus[3] which came to Mount Al-bordi (?Bardis). Yet another Persian legend tells of the Patriarch Yima[4] being warned of a coming Deluge and being told to take representatives of all living things and hide in a cave in a mountain until the danger was past.[5] This cave or 'var' was square, as long as a horse could run, contained specimens of all plants, animals and birds as well as a thousand human couples, and finally had 'a window which could be opened, for the light'.[6]

From Persia we proceed to India, a land full of myths and legends. Many of these are contained in the sacred Vedas, a vast mass of religious writings reflecting streams of thought from the sixth century B.C. back even to the tenth century B.C. In one of these[7] we are told that the demon Hayagriva having stolen the Vedas from Brahma, the human race became wicked with the

48

exceptions of Satyavrata,[8] prince of Dravidia, and the seven Rishis. While the prince was washing in the river, Vishnu appeared to him as a small fish and warned him that the world would be flooded in seven days' time. Satyavrata was commanded to take food, and pairs of animals and together with the seven holy men and their wives enter a vessel which would be provided. All this came to pass and finally Satyavrata was made a god under the name Vaivaswata. The Hindus further believed that the Ark of Satyavrata came to rest half way up the mountain Chaisa-ghar[9] and even asserted that the footmarks of the dove let out from the Ark could be seen in the snow of the mountain! In the Rig-Veda (Satapatha-Brahmana) the hero Manu had to build the vessel himself.[10]

Other much cruder Deluge stories still persist in remote parts of India as, for example, among the Kamars, a tribe of Central India,[11] and in Kashmir[12] and Assam.[13] The legends become still more debased as we continue eastward. The Karens of Burma report that two brothers were saved on a raft, while the Chinghaws of Upper Burma have a man and his sister saved in a boat which contained nine cocks and nine needles! The inhabitants of Viet Nam have a brother and sister rescued from a flood in a great chest which also contained two of every kind of animal.[14] Thus, indeed, we might continue to the remotest confines of Asia. The Flood story is current in Indonesia, in Sumatra, Sarawak, New Guinea, and far into the islands of the Pacific, including the New Hebrides and Tahiti.[15] The Hawaii people report a Flood which destroyed all the wicked and from which only Nu-u and his family were saved. These made a great canoe with a house on it and took plants and animals into it. After the deluge Nu-u saw the moon which he worshipped thinking it was a god, but the god who had sent the flood came down the rainbow, reproved Nu-u, yet forgave him and left the rainbow behind. This pretty little story would seem to have come under the influence of the Biblical account but it is not possible to determine now how or when it could have reached to so remote a group of islands.

The Flood story was known in China and once again it is not easy to decide which variations are indigenous and which have been brought by, or influenced by, Nestorian Christians who are known to have penetrated far into that land. However some of the oldest legends, going back many centuries before the Christian era, speak of the Yellow Emperor who was sad because of the wicked ways of men upon whom he sent great floods. Boat builders worked day and night to save themselves and many people hid in caves. Kun, the grandson of the Yellow Emperor, took pity on mankind and, helped by the owl and the tortoise, succeeded in stealing some magic earth which absorbed the flood.[16]

Although it has sometimes been said that the Japanese had no legend of the Flood yet in their book Koji-Ki[17] the various islands of the Pacific rise above the waters of the Deluge. Even into Siberia the Flood story penetrated: the Votyaks of Western Siberia speak of Noj while the Ostyaks tell of the hero Pairachta. Each built a huge boat single-handed, Noj taking three and Pairachta thirty years. The evil one, wishing to destroy these boats which were hidden, got the builders' wives to brew strong drink and make them drunk, whereupon they babbled and told the secret. The evil one destroyed the boats but the heroes rebuilt them.[18] From Siberia the Flood legend can be followed into the Kamchatka peninsula from which it passed across the Bering Strait to America. It passed, too, beyond the limits of Asia into Australia where the primitive inhabitants believe that their hero Nurrundere punished his wicked wives and their children by a deluge,[19] and into New Zealand where the Maoris believe that man became so wicked that god stamped on the crystal floor of heaven and broke it so that the waters of the Upper World fell on the earth and drowned it.[20]

It would take far too long to record the literally scores of different Flood legends which were carried by the expanding human race across the Bering Strait into North America. The Flood story is found in the frozen north, in Alaska and among the Eskimo. It is found in well over a hundred different tribes of

Indians in North and South America.[21] Often grossly distorted but still recognizable, it reaches at last to the most southerly limit, Tierra del Fuego, where it still asserts that all the earth except one high mountain was submerged and but a few people were saved.[22] It occurs among the most primitive natives as well as among the highly civilized Aztecs. In the case of the latter the legend was already very old when the Spaniards arrived and it is believed that the account is a combination of the legends of still older races, perhaps going back to the Toltecs and to the pre-Toltec aborigines five hundred or more years earlier. Ixtlilxochitl, the native historian, says that the first world lasted 1716 years before it was destroyed by a flood.[23] He mentions also giants and earthquakes. A little later in their legends the Aztecs tell of the prophet Huemac or Quetzalcoatl who taught ethics, warned the people of coming destruction and died at the age of 300.[24] They say that a human pair, Nata and Nena, survived the Flood in a ship which they built at the command of the god Tezcatlipoca. The date of the Flood was the year Cacalli.[25]

Strange customs lingered down into almost modern times among the North American Indians. The Mandans had a curious ceremony in which one of their number wore a white wolf-skin and a head-dress made from two ravens. The ritual included a kind of sacred wooden tub which was supposed to represent the canoe in which one man alone had escaped the Flood. The Algonquin Indians believe that Michabo the Sun God sent the raven to look for some earth to remake the world after the Deluge, and even in Alaska the Louchieux Indians connect the raven with the Flood.[26]

When we turn to the continent of Africa we find that Flood stories are much less common, but it is not true to say, as some have, that there are no indigenous records of the Deluge in Africa. Recollections of the Flood and characters associated with it are to be found in the ancient writings of the Egyptians and in the traditions of various local tribes.

So far as Ancient Egypt is concerned we have several lines of

evidence. Diodorus Siculus[27] has a quaint paragraph in which
he argues that if some living creatures survived the Flood of
Deucalion it was probable that the Egyptians were among the
number. But even, he says, if all life were destroyed, Egypt was
so fertile that it would have given spontaneous birth to new life.
We cannot now tell whether this is merely the opinion of
Diodorus or whether it was shared by the Egyptians themselves.
Plato, however, records the statement of an Egyptian priest that
the gods, wishing to purify the earth by water, overwhelmed it
with a deluge. Certain herdsmen and shepherds were saved on
the tops of mountains but those who lived in towns were swept
away to sea by the overflowing rivers.[28]

Again, according to Manetho the Egyptian historian, it was
the god Thoth who set up the two columns of knowledge in the
Siriadic land before the Deluge.[29] Several other Egyptian gods
are connected with the Flood.[30] Ra, the sun-god, ordered Hathor
(Athyr) the goddess of love and the guardian of the cemeteries
of the dead, and Sekmet, goddess of fire, to destroy the rebellious
people of the world. When the world was filled with blood Ra
relented, and being unable to stop the slaughter, flooded the
world with beer which the two goddesses drank and thus forgot
their murderous mission. Here we may observe that beside the
extremely crude reference to a flood we have the idea of intoxi-
cation—as we find in the Biblical story of Noah—and of the
name Athyr, the Egyptian name of the Flood month, as well as
the idea of the guardian of the dead which we shall find again
associated with flood legends.

Still earlier was the legend of Atum, a local god of Heliopolis,
who later became merged with Ra. Atum is said to have let loose
the waters of the great deep over the Earth so that only those
who were in his boat escaped. The god, Osiris, too, is connected
with the Flood. Plutarch[31] says that Osiris was a husbandman, a
legislator and the inventor of wine. His enemy, Typhon,[32]
prevailed upon him to enter a chest the lid of which was then
closed and the box floated down the Nile to the sea. Plutarch
records the date as the 17th Athyr, the second month, the very

date of the Flood. Variations of this story are found among the Egyptians, the villain being Osiris's brother, Set, who got Osiris into a box and launched him down the Nile. Osiris, once again, is the god of the dead.

From Egypt we cross the Sudan where the natives call Lake Caudie in Barnu, Bahr el Nuh, the Lake of Noah, and on the far side of Africa meet the quaint story of the Yorubas of W. Nigeria. These folk believe that at one time Sango, the chief of the gods, lived among mortal men. He used to talk with men, satisfy their needs and grant victory to his people in war. As a special favour to his people Sango brought the sky very low so that people who were hungry needed only to take a knife and cut a little piece of the sky for their food. The only homage which people had to pay to Sango was to go on collective hunting once a year and give all the animals killed to him. After some time the people became too familiar with Sango and one year they actually forgot the hunting day. Sango was angry, raised the sky and sent rain which flooded their farmlands and destroyed the entire people, leaving only his servant through whom a new city was founded. To this day whenever a storm arises on sea voyages, elderly Yorubas always pray to Sango to forget the neglect of years gone by. Other variations tell of the one righteous man being saved by high walls around his settlement.

Further south crude Flood stories are reported from the Congo[33] and the Basuto tribes. Finally the Hottentots of South Africa believe that they are descended from Noh and Hingnoh[34] while the Nama Hottentots have a deluge story which includes a 'swimming house'.[35]

The Flood story came to Europe as it had done to each of the other continents. It came to the Greeks but no one now knows either when or how. Homer[36] speaks of the 'rainbow that the son of Kronos hath set in the clouds, a marvel of the tribes of mortal man' which seems to be a recollection of the words[37] 'I do set my bow in the cloud and it shall be for a token of a covenant between me and the earth'.

The Greeks (Hellenes) recognized Hellen as one of their

remote ancestors. Hellen was the son of Deukalion and Deukalion[38] was involved in a deluge. It is possible, but by no means certain, that a person of such a name was involved in a local flood[39] and that, as sometimes happens, his story became merged with legends of the great Flood. The story is alluded to by Pindar[40] and Apollodorus[41] and is best known from Ovid's *Metamorphosis*.[42] In these accounts Zeus decided to destroy the human race by floods which drowned all except a few who escaped to the mountains. Deukalion, advised by his father Prometheus and accompanied by his wife Pyrrha, took refuge in a vessel loaded with provisions. The flood which then descended is graphically described by Ovid:[43]

'Sea and land have no distinction. All is sea but a sea without a shore. Here one man seeks a hill-top in his flight; another sits in his curved skiff plying the oars where lately he has ploughed; one sails over his fields of grain or the roof of his buried farm-house and one takes fish caught in the elm trees top . . . The Nereids are amazed to see beneath the waters groves and cities and the haunts of men . . . The wolf swims among the sheep while tawny lions and tigers are borne along by the waves . . . and the wandering bird, after long searching for a place to alight, falls with weary wings into the sea . . . The sea, in unchecked liberty has now buried all the hills, and strange waves beat upon the mountain peaks. Most living things are drowned outright. Those who have escaped the water, slow starvation at last overcomes through lack of food.'[44]

There is reason to believe, too, that the legends of the Argo include much older material, the original ship being acknowledged by the Greeks as the first ship, and the Hindu Argha, which it resembles, being also a recollection of the Ark.[45] Plutarch mentions the dove in connection with the Flood while Plato believed in the drowning of an ancient world-empire, Atlantis—a subject fascinating indeed, but too vast and vague for inclusion here[46]. Finally, in Greece, Bacchus, the god of wine, seems plainly a confused recollection of Noah. He was, like Osiris, enclosed in a chest, rescued from the sea, he instructed men in agriculture, was a husbandman, and was represented as sailing in a ship decked with leaves of ivy and vine[47].

From Greece the Flood story came to the Romans. Among the many gods of Rome was Janus the accounts of whose history are somewhat confused. Janus was the god who looked both ways— back into the past, the Old World, and forward into the future, to a new era. Like Noah he belonged to both. He became not only the god of doors but of the opening of the Year—hence January. Janus, the two-headed god was called the Father of the World and also the Inventor of Ships. Presents given on his festivals include copper coins[48] with the head of Janus on one side and a part of a ship on the other, or in some cases a dove with a branch in its mouth.

The ever-expanding human tribes came at last to the North of Europe and to Iceland bringing ancient sagas and legends with them. These vast and weird stories are collected mainly in the Eddas, books which in some places enshrine Norse stories from pre-Christian times. No one now knows when they were originally put together but they tell of huge struggles between the gods, the Aesir, and the Fire and Frost Giants. They tell of a flood either by sea or by the blood of a giant and of the escape of Bergelmir and his wife in a ship.[49] The Norse god Odin was also the god of the dead and besides having two raven-messengers, Huginn and Munninn,[50] was a so-called 'Raven-god'. The raven long remained as a sign on Viking ships.

Remains of a flood story are found in Lithuania,[51] Finland[52] and Lapland[53] and if we may come at last to our own lands they were to be found here before the coming of Christianity. In Wales it was the overflowing of Llyn Llion from which only Dwyvan and Dwyvach escaped, whilst in Ireland Bith and his family alone escaped the deluge and came at last in a ship to Inisfail.[54]

The Flood story has indeed reached to the ends of the Earth.[55] It extends across Asia from Turkey to Siberia, China, Japan[56] and Indonesia. It is found in Australia, New Zealand and the Islands of the Pacific. It is prolific in its various forms in both North and South America, from Alaska to Tierra del Fuego. It

E

is rarer in Africa though yet to be found from Egypt to Nigeria and from the Congo to the Cape. Finally it has crossed Europe from Greece to Ireland and Iceland. In some cases it bears evidence of having been influenced or even introduced by Jewish traders or early Christian travellers. In some cases the old Babylonian story itself may have been recounted in neighbouring lands—but allowing for all of this it remains true that there is no other story of an ancient event in all the world so widely accepted. The cumulative weight of this evidence is that the present human race has spread from one centre and even from one family—a family who themselves experienced the great Deluge of which every story speaks.

NOTES

1. Koran, c. xi.
2. G. S. Faber, *Horae Mosaicae*, p. 104.
3. Or wise man. Cf. Atrahasis, the very wise. He is called the second father of mankind.
4. Cf. The Norse Ymer.
5. E. Sykes, *Dictionary of non-classical Mythology*, p. 244.
6. Larousse, *Encyclopaedia of Mythology*, p. 332.
7. G. S. Faber, *Horae Mosaicae*, p. 106.
8. Satya the Righteous.
9. G. S. Faber, *Horae Mosaicae*, p. 127. Other accounts say the Ark went to Mt. Himarat (Himalayas).
10. H. S. Bellamy, *Moons, Myths and Man*, p. 124.
11. J. G. Frazer, *Folk-lore in the Old Testament*, p. 79.
12. H. S. Bellamy, *Moons, Myths and Man*, p. 107.
13. J. G. Frazer, *Folk-lore in the Old Testament*, p. 80.
14. J. G. Frazer, *Folk-lore in the Old Testament*, pp. 80–82.
15. J. G. Frazer, *Folk-lore in the Old Testament*, pp. 82–92.
16. C. Birch, *Chinese Myths and Fantasies*, p. 20. (London 1961). The actual references come from the Shu-King, a collection of ancient documents made by Confucius (about 500 B.C. and therefore free from any Christian missionary influence). The date there ascribed to the Emperor Yao and the time of the Flood is 2300 B.C.
17. E. Sykes, *Dictionary of non-classical Mythology*, p. 119.
18. H. S. Bellamy, *Moons, Myths and Man*, p. 126.
19. E. Sykes, ibid., p. 157.
20. H. S. Bellamy, ibid., p. 109.
21. See J. G. Frazer, *Folk-lore in the Old Testament*, pp. 110–128 and E. Sykes, *Dictionary of non-classical Mythology*.
22. J. G. Frazer, *ibid.* p. 107.
23. G. C. Vaillant, *The Aztecs of Mexico*, p. 68.
24. Compare the Phrygian Annakos or Enoch.
25. E. Sykes, *Dictionary of non-classical Mythology*, pp. 24, 149. The Mixtecs, the Zapotecs and the Mayas also had Flood stories. See Helmut de Terra, *Man and Mammoth in Mexico*, pp. 122–146.

26. E. A. Armstrong, *The Folk-lore of Birds*, p. 89.
27. Bk. 1. Ch. 1.
28. Plato, *Timaeus*, Trans. by H. D. P. Lee, pp. 32–38.
29. E. Sykes, *Dictionary of non-classical Mythology*, p. 195. Josephus, *Antiquities*, Bk. 1. Ch. II, Section 3, attributed the construction of the two Siriadic Astronomical columns to Seth, son of Adam, and says they survived the Deluge. There is a similarity here with Xisuthros writing the history of the beginning, procedure and end of all things, on tablets which were buried at Sippar and which survived the Flood.
30. E. Sykes, *ibid.*, pp. 66, 67.
31. Plutarch, *De Isid*, Quoted from *Horae Mosaicae*, p. 140.
32. Typhon was probably a personification of the sea.
33. Larousse, *Encyclopaedia of Mythology*, p.485. J. G. Frazer, *Folk-lore in the Old Testament*, p. 129.
34. A. M. Rehwinkel, *The Flood*, p. 129.
35. H. S. Bellamy, *Moons, Myths and Man*, p. 128.
36. *Iliad*, xi. 28.
37. Genesis 9. 13.
38. Deukalion means 'new-wine sailor'. R. Graves, *The Greek Myths*, (Index).
39. Aristotle says at Dodona.
40. ol. 9. 41.
41. Quoted from Skinner, *Genesis*, p. 179, but the *Encyclopaedia Britannica*, 9. 456 says the work in question is wrongly ascribed to Apollodorus.
42. Ovid, *Metam.*, i. 244–415.
43. Ovid, *Metamorphoses*, From Translation by F. J. Miller, Loeb Classical Library, i. 283–312.
44. Deucalion's ark rested on Parnassus. But Parnassus was anciently called Larnassus (Brewer, *Dictionary of Phrase and Fable*) because Deucalion's Ark is called by Plutarch, Lucian, and Apollodorus, Larnax, the Chest or Coffin. This of course links again with Osiris and also with the Greek KIBOTOS, box, for the Ark. (Gen. 6. 15 LXX).
45. G. S. Faber, *Horae Mosaicae*, p. 132 ff.
46. Plato refers to the Deluge in the *Timaeus*, claiming that the information came from the Egyptians. See p. 52. See also Clem. Alex., *The Miscellanies*, Bk. 1. Ch. 21.
47. G. S. Faber, *ibid.*, p. 142.
48. *Dictionary of Greek and Roman Biography*, Vol. II. p. 551. A. Hislop, *The Two Babylons*, pp. 135, 136.
49. The god Njord was the god of ships and an Edda poem says that he lived at Noatun—the enclosure or harbour of ships. The so-called Vanir gods possessed ships, and the ship became associated with death. Ritual ship-burials are illustrated by the find at Sutton Hoo.
    See H. R. Ellis Davidson, *Gods and Myths of Northern Europe*. The ship Naglfar was said to have been made from the nails of dead men. Hringhorn the ship of Balder was said to have been larger than Naglfar.
50. Hugginn and Munninn may represent mind and memory.
51. E. Sykes, *Dictionary of non-classical Mythology*, p. 126.
52. E. Sykes, *Dictionary of non-classical Mythology*, p. 114.
53. B. C. Nelson, *The Deluge Story in Stone*, p. 180.
54. E. Sykes, *Dictionary of non-classical Mythology*, p. 47. H. Peake, *The Flood*, p. 15 ff. dismisses some of the Celtic legends because in their present form they cannot be traced back to pre-Christian times. But while this is true of *written* accounts, and while some legends may have been modified since the coming of Christianity it remains true that the Celtic legends are very old, some of them of immense antiquity. The keeping of Samhain in November is the final proof that the Celtic recollection of the Flood goes back far before the coming of Christianity. See p. 108.

55. Dr. Richard Andree collected 88 Flood stories, 20 Asiatic, 5 European, 7 African, 10 Australasian and Pacific and 46 American. He concludes that 62 of them are independent of the Babylonian or Hebrew accounts.

H. S. Bellamy in *Moons, Myths and Man* estimates that altogether there are over 500 Flood legends. About 70 can be found in Sykes's *Dictionary of non-classical Mythology*.

56. It is sometimes stated that the Japanese have no Flood story but the Deluge comes in the story Koji Ki. See E. Sykes, *Dictionary*, pp. 119–120.

It is curious too, that the Chinese symbols for a large ship are the two symbols 'Eight' and 'Mouths' or 'persons'.

CHAPTER 4

THE AUTHENTICITY AND AUTHORSHIP OF
THE BIBLICAL ACCOUNT

WE come now to a consideration of the actual Biblical account
of the Flood. This is contained essentially in Genesis chapters
6–9 which we shall study in detail, but, before doing so, it may
be well to examine the other Biblical and ancient Jewish
references to the event. As the Hebrew word *mabbul* used of the
Flood in Genesis occurs only again in Psalm 29.10 that passage
has been quoted by some as referring to the Noachian deluge. It
seems, however, to be rather a general assertion of the power of
God over storms and floods. We read:

> v. 3. The voice of the Lord is upon the waters,
>   The God of glory thunders,
>   The Lord is upon many waters.
> v. 10. The Lord sits enthroned over the flood (*mabbul*),
>   The Lord sits enthroned as King for ever.

It is worth noting that the writer here uses both titles, YHWH
and EL, for the Creator, but no thoughtful person would assert
that this proves two different authors for verse 3, nor does the
repetition of thought so plainly manifest in this, as in so many
other Old Testament poetical passages, prove anything more
than to demonstrate the rhythm that is characteristic of Hebrew
poetry.

There is a definite reference to the Flood in Isaiah 54. 9.
RSV where we read: 'For this is like the days of Noah to me,
as I swore that the waters of Noah should no more go over the
earth' . . . Here there is a plain reference to God's covenant
with Noah which is interpreted as a Divine oath. The prophet

59

Ezekiel (ch. 14 vv. 14, 20) declares that in his time Israel was so sinful that even had Noah been alive then he would not have been able to deliver his own family . . . from which it is evident that in Ezekiel's days the Jews regarded Noah as an outstanding historical example of righteousness.[1]

Another ancient Jewish writer who shows a knowledge of the Flood is the author of the apocryphal Wisdom of Solomon (Wisdom 10. 1–4, RV) 'But when an unrighteous man fell away from wisdom in his anger, he perished himself in the rage wherewith he slew his brother, and when for his cause the earth was drowning with a Flood, Wisdom again saved it, guiding the righteous man's course by a poor piece of wood'. In Wisdom chapters 13 and 15 the author attacks idolatry along the same lines as does Isaiah in Isaiah 44: men take the wood and use part for useful things, part for burning and part for idols which they worship. The writer goes on (Wisdom 14. 5, RV) 'Therefore also do men entrust their lives to a little piece of wood, and passing through the surge on a raft are brought safe to land. For in the olden time also, when proud giants were perishing, the hope of the world, taking refuge on a raft, left to the race of men a seed of generations to come, Thy hand guiding the helm'.

In the writings of Jesus ben Sirach, Ecclesiasticus, we have two references to the Flood, one very brief (ch. 16. 7) referring to the destruction of the Nephilim, and the other (ch. 44. 17–18) being taken almost verbatim from the Genesis account. In this well-known chapter on famous men the writer declares 'Noah was found perfect and righteous; in the season of wrath he was taken in exchange for the world: therefore was there left a remnant unto the earth when the Flood came; everlasting covenants were made with him, that all flesh should no more be blotted out by a flood'.

We shall pass over various other references in Jewish pseudepigraphical literature such as the so-called books of Enoch and Noah, books of diverse and doubtful authorship and very late date,[2] and consider next the references in the New

Testament. These are as follows: Matthew 24. 37–39, RV 'And as were the days of Noah, so shall be the coming of the Son of man. For as in those days which were before the Flood they were eating and drinking, marrying and giving in marriage, until the day that Noah entered into the ark, and they knew not until the Flood came, and took them all away; so shall be the coming of the Son of man'. This passage is given also in Luke 17. 26, 27. In Hebrews 11. 7 the writer asserts 'By faith, Noah being warned of God concerning things not seen as yet, moved with godly fear, prepared an ark to the saving of his house, through which he condemned the world, and became heir of the righteousness which is according to faith'. Finally we have in I Peter 3. 20 the statement that 'the longsuffering of God waited in the days of Noah, while the ark was a preparing, wherein few, that is eight, souls were saved through water', and in II Peter 2. 5 'God spared not the ancient world, but preserved Noah with seven others, a preacher of righteousness, when He brought a flood upon the world of the ungodly'.[3]

From these references it is clear that Christ and His disciples accepted the Genesis account of the Flood without any hesitation or question. While there are some modern writers who assert that Christ voluntarily restricted His knowledge and conformed to the general views of His era, even if these were erroneous, there are others of us who cannot accept such a contention. He who could spend hours in converse with the Eternal Father[4] and who on the Mountain could maintain conversation with the timeless spirits of Moses and Elijah, who could foresee the future . . . His own death, the fall of Jerusalem, the spread of the Church throughout the world despite age-long persecution, the character of the last days, so similar to those of Noah's . . . He must have known the truth concerning the past as well as the future, the truth of the Flood as well as of the greater judgment yet to come.

The Genesis story was, then, widely known throughout Jewish History and accepted without question as true. It was the accepted view, too, of the Jewish people that the Genesis account was

written or compiled by Moses and this was accepted by the
Church Fathers[5] and later Christian writers for the next 1500
years. By the time of the Reformation, however, various views
of the authorship of the Pentateuch were promulgated by Roman
Catholic, Protestant and Jewish theologians. The philosopher
Spinoza, 1670, considered that Ezra was possibly the compiler of
the Pentateuch. A little-known writer, H. B. Witter in 1711
suggested that two documents lay behind Genesis 1–3 and he
gave the different forms of the name of God as the criterion for
distinguishing these. Jean Astruc (1753) concluded that Moses
had used two older documents one of which employed the title
Jehovah and the other Elohim, but he soon found that this theory
would not fit the facts and he was compelled to introduce eleven
more sources for the Pentateuch. For the next two hundred years
writer succeeded writer in removing more and more of the
Pentateuch from Moses and his times—some even asserting
that Moses could not write—critics vying with each other to
discover fresh compilers, editors and revisers of the early books
of the Bible. While these critics differed widely from each other
the majority in more recent times have paid at least lip-service to
the so-called Development Hypothesis of Karl Heinrich Graf,
Abraham Kuenan and Julius Wellhausen. These views were
borrowed, and slightly modified, by the British writers, S. R.
Driver and John Skinner in their respective commentaries on
Genesis. Although almost all of the theories on which these views
were erected have been shown to be questionable, and despite
the almost incredible hypotheses used to bolster them up, they
are still dogmatically propagated by numerous theologians as if
they were still valid. It will not come within the scope of this
work to examine the Graf-Wellhausen Hypothesis as applied to
the whole Pentateuch but only to consider it in relation to the
account of the Flood. Here we may select the analysis given by
Skinner in his commentary. There are, he asserts (p. 147) two
separate Flood stories which the 'compiler' has woven into one,
'preserving in the process many duplicates as well as leaving
unaltered many striking differences of representation and

phraseology'.[6] Skinner adds, 'the resolution of the compound narrative into its constituent elements in this is justly reckoned among the most brilliant achievements of purely literary criticism'. After this very modest opinion of the critics' work by one of themselves the writer proceeds to give the result of this vivisection of the Genesis story. The two 'sources' which the compiler or 'Redactor, R^{JP}' has so cunningly interwoven are called J and P. But no one knows who J was. Some think that he was a person, others, a school of writers. Some think that he must be dated about the ninth century B.C.[7] but others think that J is a very complex source, parts of which are now even admitted to be of the Mosaic—or even pre-Mosaic era! Some have subdivided J into J[1], J[2], etc., while another leading critic[8] has invented a new source for part of J which he calls L and to which he attributes the story of Noah's drunkenness.

The other source P (Priestly Code) is again described[9] as 'manifestly the work of a school or succession of writers . . . yet it bears the impress of a single mind and must be treated as a unity'. Skinner and most others attribute P to about 500 B.C. but so late as 1934 Gerhard von Rad decided that the section which Skinner says bears so obviously the impress of a single mind is really the work of two individuals, P^a and P^b, while in 1941 R. H. Pfeiffer found a new author altogether, 'S', in the first eleven chapters of Genesis. All this makes one very sceptical of the 'most brilliant achievements' of the literary critics! To take, however, Skinner's analysis of the Flood story, we have the following:

J. Ch. 6. 1–8, Ch. 7. 1–5, (8, 9.) 10, 12, 16^b, 17^b, 22, 23. Ch. 8. 2^b, 3^a, 6–12, 13^b, 20–22.
P. The remainder.

Anyone who will take the time and trouble to underline in an old Bible the sections thus attributed to J, leaving the remainder not underlined, and who will then read the comments of Skinner and one or two other critics, will be able to satisfy himself of the utter futility of such a division of the Flood story. The whole account is ruined by this vivisection and the conclusions drawn from this highly improbable dissection are in some cases absurd.

Arguments that in the two accounts there are differences in style are of little value. It is characteristic of all great authors that they can vary their style, and ancient writers just as much as any modern ones always sought to avoid monotony.[10] Variations in style can be seen just as clearly in ancient Egyptian and Babylonian works as well as, for example, in Homer where no-one now suspects multiple authorship. The 200-year-old argument that there must be two authors J, and P, because of the two divine names YHWH and ELOHIM is also of no value whatever. The word ELOHIM is used in Genesis 6. 2 which Skinner, in his commentary on that section, assigns to J. It is used in ch. 7. verse 9 where it causes Skinner such embarrass-ment that he supposed 'J's narrative has here been taken to pieces by the Redactor who has fitted the fragments into a new connexion supplied by the combined accounts of J and P'. It is difficult to see what to make of such a futile statement. Even yet more devastating for the critics is v. 16 of ch. 7 where we read 'they that went in, went in male and female of all flesh as GOD commanded him: and the LORD shut him in'. Skinner's feeble reply is that P wrote one half of the verse and J the other half! Again six of the sections which Skinner assigns to J do not con-tain the name YHWH so that they have been attributed to J by other forms of guesswork. It has been further pointed out that in a single Egyptian stela of 1800 B.C. four different names or titles are given to Osiris[11], yet no thoughtful person supposes four authors. Again the Kamose Stela in Egypt contains five different terms for boats[12] showing the preference of ancient writers for variety within a single document.

As Skinner's division now stands it appears that in J's account the Lord commands Noah to enter an ark which He has not yet told him to build, and at the close of the narrative Noah builds an altar but has not yet left the ark. The critics naïvely get over this by asserting that of course the Redactor used only a part of J and a part of P 'in order to avoid repetitions' . . . yet they started from the argument that there must be two authors because there are repetitions! In fact the existence of repetitions proves nothing; they are common in Eastern forms of story-telling. There are, for example, repetitions within the account which Skinner attributes to J. In ch. 6, v. 7 the LORD says that He will destroy man and beast from the face of the ground and this is repeated in ch. 7. 4. (J) when the LORD says 'I will destroy every living thing from the face of the ground'. There are repetitions, too, within the parts ascribed to P, for example in ch. 6, verse 17 repeats verse 13 and in ch. 7 we are twice told (vv. 7 and 13) that Noah went into the ark. On this absurd 'repetition hypothesis' then we have proof of at least four writers, J^1, J^2, P^1, P^2. Again the critics' statement that P is concerned with exact measurements while J is graphic and poetical are just as useless. By the arbitrary cutting up of the story, as mentioned above, they have left J no ark to measure. The argument about the pairs of animals will be dealt with in its place,[13] and the arguments that J thought the whole Flood lasted only 40 days because of ch. 8. 6 is really too feeble to bother to refute.[14] The 'most brilliant achievements' of this subjective method of literary criticism are, in fact, worthless. They are of the same type as those used by the 'super-intellectuals' who believe that the Iliad was not written by Homer and that Bacon wrote Shakespeare's plays.[15] While one appreciates all true scholarship and the careful scrutiny of ancient records the J-P theory of the Genesis Flood account must surely rank as one of the most outstanding examples of human fallibility. As Derek Kidner (*Genesis* p. 100) says in his penetrating criticism of these theories, 'To turn from these elaborate exercises to the narrative itself is, we may suggest, to move from the realm of the ingeniously improbable into the fresh air of simplicity and truth.

We may dismiss the theory that the Genesis account of the Flood is the work of some fourth- or fifth-century B.C. redactor R^{JP} and return to the much more reasonable view that it was written nearly a thousand years earlier by Moses. It is quite true

that there is no statement in Genesis itself to the effect that it
was written by Moses but our Lord and His disciples refer to
the Pentateuch as the work of Moses;[16] it was so recognized in
the Old Testament;[17] the ancient Jewish writers and commentators[18] have never doubted the Mosaic authorship and early
Gentile writers have accepted this as a fact.[19] Hebrew scholars
have long maintained that both the general similarity of style and
the undesigned coincidences of expression show the Pentateuch
to be a unity.[20] The writer was a Hebrew, acquainted with the
Egyptian customs and language, and the existence of archaic
forms of Hebrew words and very ancient names for places show
the great antiquity of the account.[21] The entire work of the
Pentateuch is the work of a genius—a fact obscured by the
Higher Critical controversy—a genius to be compared only with
Homer, Dante and Shakespeare.[22] As Dr. W. J. Martin truly
points out,[23] it is rare that one nation produces more than one
such writer. To ask us to believe that Israel produced a group of
such geniuses—all anonymous then, and still unknown to this
day—is really asking too much. Is it not more probable that the
Pentateuch as we have it today comes to us almost as Moses
left it?

Now this does not mean, of course, that men like Moses,
Homer and Shakespeare did not draw on older sources for
historical information. Everyone recognizes that they did, and
this does not detract from the evidences of genius running
through their work. In the case of the Flood the event itself was
so far back in human history that, as we have seen, there were
but few sources of information. The study of the Biblical account
shows—as we shall see—that it is based on a record which, in the
ultimate, is that of an eye-witness of the actual events. The
minute details, some now difficult to translate, show plainly that
the account is derived from a first-hand very ancient record—i.e.
that of Noah himself or of Shem. This record was transmitted to
Shem's descendants, probably orally for some generations until
the development of writing enabled it to be recorded. The purest
form of the story remained with the descendants of Arphaxad

while the more distorted forms were mingled with the rising myths of other Semitic and Hamitic peoples who inhabited the land of the two rivers. The story carefully preserved by Abraham was passed on to his descendants through Isaac and Jacob until it was incorporated at last into the Mosaic history of pre-Abrahamic times.

NOTES

1. Amos 5.8. and 9.6. 'The Lord calleth for the waters of the sea and poureth them out upon the face of the earth', may be a reference to the Flood (so E. B. Pusey, *The Minor Prophets*, in loc.). Others think this a reference to the evaporation of sea water and its return as rain on the land. (See *New Bible Commentary*, I.V.F.).

2. These range from second to third century B.C. to some which are first century A.D. A few are quoted on pp. 71f.

3. See also II Peter 3.6.

4. John 12.48–50.

5. See E. J. Young, *Introduction to the Old Testament*, Chapter 2 and chapter 7 for a very full examination of the Higher Critical Theories of the Pentateuch and a wide selection of relevant references. Jerome was no real exception though he speaks of Ezra as re-editing the Pentateuch.
    See also D. Kidner's acute analysis of the weakness of the so-called Literary Criticism of the Pentateuch, whose methods he describes as 'miracles of surgery'. *Genesis Introduction*, pp. 16–22.

6. This he has quoted from S. R. Driver's *Commentary*, p. 85.

7. S. R. Driver, *Genesis*, p. xvi.

8. Otto Eissfeldt, in *Hexateuch-Synopse*, (1922).

9. J. Skinner, *Genesis*, p. lviii.

10. See W. J. Martin, *Stylistic Criteria and the Analysis of the Pentateuch*, (London 1955).

11. The Berlin Stela of Ikhernofret. See K. A. Kitchen, *New Bible Dictionary*, Art. Egypt, p. 349, and Review of J. Vergote's *Joseph en Égypte* in Journal of Egyptian Archaeology, (Vol. 47) (1961), p. 163.

12. K. A. Kitchen, *ibid.*, p. 163 and *Ancient Orient & Old Testament*, Ch. 6.

13. P. 98. See also W. J. Martin, *Stylistic Criteria and the Analysis of the Pentateuch*, p. 15 and D. Kidner, *Genesis*, p. 89, Note 4.

14. Chronological considerations are dealt with in detail on pp. 103ff.

15. Similar exercises can be carried out to show that *Alice in Wonderland* is the work of several authors and even *Winnie the Pooh* is based on two earlier manuscripts, *Er-Winnie* and *Proto-Pooh* carefully worked together by the Redactor R^{WP} or A. A. Milne! The method has also been used to show that Abraham Lincoln could not have composed the Gettysburg speech!

16. H. H. Rowley, *The Old Testament and Modern Study*, p. xvii. Mark 7. 12; 12. 26; Luke 5. 14; 16. 29, 31; 20. 37; 24. 27, 44; John 1. 17, 45; 3. 14; 5. 45, 46; 7. 19; Acts 3. 22; 15. 21; 26. 22; Romans 10. 5; II Corinthians 3. 15, etc.

17. Among others: Joshua 1. 3, 7; Judges 3. 4; I Kings 2. 3; 8. 53; II Kings 14. 6; I Chronicles 6. 49; II Chronicles 8. 13, Ezra 3. 2; 6. 18; 7. 6; Nehemiah 1. 7; Daniel 9. 11, 13; Malachi, 4. 4.

18. See references in Horne's, *Introduction to the Scriptures*, Vol. 1. p. 50.

19. E.g. Manetho, Eupolemus, Artapanus, Tacitus, Diodorus Siculus, Strabo and others. See Horne, *Introduction*, Vol. 1. pp. 53, 54.

20. See J. J. Blunt, *The Veracity of the Five Books of Moses argued from the undesigned coincidences to be found in them.*

21. The first eleven chapters of Genesis contain Babylonian words, the last fourteen Egyptian . . . just as we should expect if the ultimate information is based on first hand records. Some place names, e.g. Bela (which is Zoar) Siddim (which is the Salt Sea) are so old as to need the accompanying explanations. See other examples in P. J. Wiseman, *New Discoveries in Babylonia about Genesis*, (2nd. Edn.) pp. 61–65. Wiseman thinks that the reference in Gen. 23. 2 'Kirjath-arba which is Hebron in the land of Canaan' must have been written before the entry into the land or there would be no need to say where Hebron was. For other archaisms see J. Angus, *The Bible Handbook*, (New Edition, S. G. Green), p. 391, and Horne, Vol 1. p. 57.

22. That the last chapter of Deuteronomy and one or two other tiny passages have been added later by Joshua, Ezra or others is freely admitted. It does not in the least affect the main argument.

23. *Stylistic Criteria*, p. 22.

CHAPTER 5

THE BACKGROUND OF THE FLOOD

THE story of the Flood in Genesis 6 is introduced by a section which is obviously designed to give us the reason for that great disaster. On the physical level, as we have seen, the reasons must be sought in the sinking of land masses and the rise of the sea-level due to isostatic movements of land, the melting of ice-caps and other such phenomena accompanied by prolonged rain and the discharge of subterranean waters or by tides raised by some astronomical intervention. But the Bible is primarily concerned with moral and spiritual causes which run side by side with physical events in the providential dealings of the Creator. The passage in Genesis 6. 1–12 is admittedly difficult both to trans-late and to interpret. But despite these difficulties, which we shall consider in detail shortly, the main contention of vv. 5–12 is perfectly clear. The Flood was God's judgment on human wickedness. This is in complete accord with the views expressed in the New Testament. So deeply ingrained in the minds of Noah and his sons was this fact that, as the new races spread across the world, carrying with them the various recollections of the Flood, this conception of human wickedness is frequently given as the reason for the disaster. It can be found even in remote corners of the earth associated with the Deluge story, sometimes in the form that men had angered the gods or rebelled against them, at other times that the world had grown old or dirty or corrupt and needed to be purified. This wickedness of mankind is described in vv. 5–12 under three headings: (1) Evil thoughts (2) corruption (3) violence. That evil thoughts would lead to corruption and violence is obvious. The word for corrupt and corruption in the Old Testament is *shachath* and this can be applied to physical corruption, or, as a metaphor, to moral or religious corruption. It is frequently used of Israel when the people fell into idolatry or when they denied the existence of God.[1] The ultimate end of physical corruption is, of course, complete destruction, and the word *shachath* carries this meaning as well. Thus we have the dreadful sequence: Genesis 6. 11. The earth also was corrupt (*shachath*) before God . . . v. 17. 'Behold I do bring a flood of waters upon the earth to destroy (*shachath*) all flesh'.

Genesis 6 then implies a moral corruption of some kind infecting the human race and calling for the judgment of God. With the spread of moral corruption violence was to be expected. The word implies oppression, the physical tyranny of men over one another. It had already been seen in the Bible in Cain and Lamech and it is very clear in heathen mythology concerning the supposed early days of the gods whose doings are filled with crude violence. Archaeological evidences are not wanting that early man practised and suffered violence.

Despite the long-continued striving of the Spirit of God, whether through conscience, or the witness of Noah, corruption became so widespread that the Creator was forced to intervene. Thus far all is plain enough. But the opening verses of Genesis 6 seem intended to give us some additional information about this wickedness. Although no part of our later interpretation of the Flood account is in any way dependent upon our views of these verses yet they are an integral part of the story and we must give them fair consideration. The two opening sections of the Flood story deal with (*a*) the sons of God and the daughters of men and (*b*) the appearance on earth of the nephilim and the men of renown.

We are told in Genesis 6. 1 that the events belong to the time when men began to multiply on the face of the Earth. Such an expression could hardly apply to the early Palaeolithic but would be true of the close of the Palaeolithic Age by which time the human race had spread as far as Britain, North Africa and China.

We have already concluded that the Flood came at such a period in history.

We are then told in a very brief statement that at that time the 'sons of God saw the daughters of men (or man) that they were fair (i.e. good-looking)', and that they took them wives of all which they chose. There have been several theories as to the identity of these 'sons of God', but only two are really worthy of serious consideration. The earlier view was that they were angelic beings while in the later view they were descendants of Seth, the daughters of men being women of Cain's family.[2] Books have actually been written on this subject and it is worth repeating that the subsequent understanding of the Flood account is not really affected by the interpretation of this section. The facts seem to be as follows. The term 'daughters of men' or 'daughters of man' is, in Hebrew, 'daughters of Adam'. It cannot then be arbitrarily restricted to women of Cain's family, especially when we remember that Adam had other sons and daughters,[3] but must apply to human women in general. This gives a *prima facie* suggestion that the 'sons of elohim' . . . sons of the mighty ones . . . were rather to be contrasted with the human race. So indeed the earliest interpreters uniformly took the passage. The expression *bene-ha-elohim* is a pre-Israelite term meaning 'mighty ones' or 'gods' rather than sons of God or sons of the gods.[4] The same expression occurs in Job 1. 6 and 2. 1 in both of which cases it refers to angelic beings, and the Aramaic equivalent occurs in Daniel 3. 25 where Nebuchadnezzar discerned within the furnace the form of a fourth person like (RV) 'a son of the gods' and he interprets this term in v. 28 as 'angel'. The Septuagint translators of Job 1. 6 and 2. 1 render the expression 'angels of God'. The Codex Alexandrinus and three later manuscripts read 'angels of God' instead of sons of God in Genesis 6.[5] The view that these sons of elohim were fallen angelic beings is common throughout all the most ancient extra-Biblical literature. In Enoch 6. 1–7. 4 we have, 'And it came to pass when the children of men had multiplied that in those days were born unto them beautiful daughters. And the

angels, the children, saw and lusted after them . . . and took unto
themselves wives, and each chose for himself . . . and they bore
giants.' An ancient fragment of the 'Book of Noah' says: 'I, Enoch
have already made known to thee that in the generation of my
father Jared some of the angels transgressed the word of the Lord
. . . and united themselves with women . . . and have begotten
children of them . . . and shall produce giants . . .' The so-
called Testament of Reuben (about 150–100 B.C.) ch. 5, v. 6 says:
'For thus they (women) allured the Watchers[6] who were before
the Flood who changed themselves into the form of men . . . and
the women gave birth to giants'. The book of Jubilees, Second
Baruch and an ancient 'Zadokite' fragment which resembles the
Dead Sea Scrolls, all give the same interpretation. Philo,
Josephus and the Targum of Jonathan likewise interpret the sons
of god as angels.

The passage in Genesis 6 is also undoubtedly related to two
passages in the New Testament; II Peter 2. 4 and Jude 6. The
former of these in the Revised Version reads: 'For if God spared
not angels when they sinned, but cast them down to hell, and
committed them to pits of darkness, to be reserved unto judgment; and spared not the ancient world, but preserved Noah . . .'
The margin notes that the word 'hell' in this case is the
Greek, Tartarus. In fact it is the only reference to Tartarus in
the Bible, (except in the LXX. e.g. Job 40. 15; 41. 23), and
Tartarus was the place according to Hesiod where the Titans
were kept in chains of darkness. This connection we shall follow
a little later. Jude (v. 6, RV) says, 'And angels which kept not
their own principality, but left their proper habitation, He hath
kept in everlasting bonds under darkness unto the judgment of
the great day. Even as Sodom and Gomorrah, and the cities
round them, having in like manner with these given themselves
over to fornication, and gone after strange flesh, are set forth as
an example, suffering the punishment of eternal fire'. It has been
pointed out by commentators that the word 'them' in the phrase
'cities round about them' is feminine and refers to the cities of
Sodom and Gomorrah. The word 'these' in the phrase 'in like

manner with these' is masculine and refers back to the main subject, the angels of v. 6 for which the Greek is masculine. Dean Alford in his *Greek Testament* maintains that the Greek construction here demands such a view and he adds: 'in like manner with these, Τούτοις, the angels above mentioned. The manner was similar because the angels committed fornication with another race than themselves'. J. B. Mayor *Commentary on Jude*, Dean Farrar, W. Kelly *Ep. Jude*, Fleming *The Fallen Angels* and the *New Bible Commentary* (I.V.F.), among many others, agree with this interpretation of II Peter 2. 4 and Jude 6.

But this early view that the 'sons of elohim' were angels gave rise later to some anxiety in the Christian Church particularly when the heresy of angel-worship became a danger. Hence we find Julius Africanus adopting the view that the sons of elohim were descendants of the pious Seth and the daughters of man were descended from Cain. Chrysostom and Theodoret accepted this view because, forgetting the New Testament teaching that spirit-beings (demons) could inhabit and control human beings and that angels can appear in human form, they denied that angels could have feelings comparable with those of sex. While it is clear that unfallen angels neither 'marry nor are given in marriage' this is not relevant in considering what might happen to fallen spirit-beings. Thus despite the fact that the 'fallen angel' view had been held almost uniformly for the first three centuries, and that by men like Justyn Martyr, Clement of Alexandria, Irenaeus and Athenagoras, the Sethite theory gradually became more popular.[7] It was held in later times by Luther, and Calvin gives it but with no satisfactory reasoning. It is still maintained by some writers and was given in the notes in the earlier edition of the Scofield Bible.[8] The Rev. J. Sidlow Baxter has a section on the subject in his *Studies in problem texts*. He seems to overlook the fact that Nebuchadnezzar in Daniel 3. 28 interprets his own use of the expression 'son of a god' as an angel, he tries to minimize and then avoid the force of the LXX evidence, fails to explain how daughters of Adam can be restricted to Cain's descendants, does not make sufficient allowance for the power of demons when they enter human beings—as described clearly in the New Testament—gives no satisfactory explanation of the Nephilim and does not really deal fairly with II Peter 2. 4 and Jude 6.

The present writer feels that although the whole subject is mysterious the evidence for the 'angel' interpretation is much the stronger and that it is not only consistent with the early Hebrew mode of expression but provides the adequate impetus for that great moral decline which brought the Flood.

The second section of Genesis 6 introductory to the Flood is also difficult to translate and to interpret. In the Revised Version it reads: 'The Nephilim (or giants) were in the earth in those days, and also after that, when the sons of God came in unto the daughters of men, and they bare children unto them: the same were the mighty men which were of old, the men of renown'. One of the difficulties seems to be to determine the force of the phrase 'and also after that'. The LXX has 'Now the giants were upon the earth in those days; and after that when the sons of God were wont to go in to the daughters of men, they bore children to them, those were the giants of old, the men of renown'. The Latin Vulgate however (Translation by Knox) has 'Giants lived on the earth in those days, when first the sons of God mated with the daughters of men and by them had children; these were the heroes whose fame has come down to us from long ago'. W. J. Beecher in Hastings' *Dictionary of the Bible* translates the passage: 'The Nephilim were in the earth in those days and also afterward, forasmuch as the sons of God used to go in to the daughters of men and they bare them children; they were the heroes that were of old, the men of name'.[9]

It thus seems clear that some of the Nephilim were the product of the union of the sons of elohim with human women . . . there were others at some other time. It seems certain, too, that these were the mighty men, the renowned, of old. In other words these were the originals of the gods and heroes of mythology and legend.[10] From these pre-flood heroes and the other great group of rebels whose sin brought the judgment of Babel the ancient world derived its gods and mythology. This at once falls into line with the constant affirmation of the ancients that the gods frequently took human wives and had semi-divine children by them. Coupling this passage with Genesis 6. 11 'The earth was filled with violence' we have again perfect agreement with every detail of the ancient mythologies which make the oldest of the gods engaged in constant strife. Here too we have the beginning of wars, the conquest of one settlement by another, a principle which re-appears soon after the Flood in the conquests of Nimrod, of Sargon of Agade and the early kings of Uruk, of Kish and of Ur. The fact that the pre-Flood 'men of renown' were destroyed and that the only details remembered of them were those handed down by Noah's sons also accounts for the heathen confusion about the ancestors and relation to each other of the gods, many of whom are confused descriptions of the great rebels of the time of Nimrod and Babel mingled with the recollections of these still earlier rebels of pre-Flood times. The Nephilim were the 'fallen ones'.[11] Evidently both the Septuagint translators and Jerome in the Vulgate considered this equivalent to the Greek 'Gigantes'. That greatness of stature is included in the term is evident from Numbers 13. 33 where the Hebrew spies report (RV) 'There we saw the Nephilim, the sons of Anak, which come of the Nephilim: and we were in our own sight as grasshoppers and so we were in their sight'. But it is necessary here to go a little deeper into the history of the Giants and Titans. Originally the Greek Gigantes were a group of rebels who opposed the Olympian gods and were destroyed by them. They were said to have been of great size[12]—hence our word 'giant'—and later writers often confused them with the Titans who were also of great size—hence our word 'titanic'. In the still later developments of mythology, when natural phenomena were attributed to the ancient gods, it is probable that they were connected with volcanoes just as Zeus was connected with thunder and lightning. The Titans or Titanides were the sons of Uranus (Heaven) and Ge (Earth) and included Cronus and Iapetus.[13] Cronus with his sickle[14] (originally of flint, though later legends speak of iron) mutilated his naked father Uranus. Cronus then ascended the throne of the gods and having married his sister Rhea, became the father of Zeus, Pluto, Poseidon, Hera and other gods. When grown up, Zeus and his brothers and sisters carried on a ten-year war against the ruling Titans and having overthrown them cast them into Tartarus. Zeus, although the youngest, became and remained the supreme god of Greece. It is fairly obvious, as H. J. Rose says in his *Handbook of Greek Mythology* that these stories were not originally Greek and probably came from further east. The later Hebrews, probably after contact with the Greeks, were familiar with the stories of the Gigantes and the Titans. The LXX in II. Sam. 5. 18, 22 translates the 'Valley of Rephaim' as the 'Valley of the Titans' whereas in I Chron. 11. 15 and 14. 9 the same region is called the 'Valley of the Gigantes'. The term is also used in the Apocrypha, Judith 16. 7 where we read:

For their mighty one did not fall by the hand of the young men,
Nor did tall giants set upon him:
But Judith the daughter of Merari made him weak . . .

As we have already seen the New Testament, too, uses terms which are connected with the same events in the references to the chains or pits of darkness and in Peter's use of the term Tartarus.

We conclude that the Bible tells of two great acts of rebellion against God, both involving ancient 'heroes and men of renown', whose exploits were later recounted, exaggerated and merged with natural phenomena, to become the gods of the heathen. The first of these great times of rebellion and wickedness brought the Flood, the second, the confusion of languages at Babel.[15] From these days and doings come the legends of Giants and Titans, Cronus and Rhea, Zeus, Herakles, gods, goddesses and demigods.

In its usual, very restrained, brief, but pregnant terms the Hebrew account, surveying the conditions which brought the Flood, records . . . 'the earth was filled with violence and every imagination of men's hearts was evil continually' (Gen. 6. 5, 13).

NOTES

1. Exod. 32. 7; Deut. 32. 5; 4. 16; 31. 29; Zeph. 3. 7; Ps. 14. 1–3.
2. There is also a Jewish view that the sons of elohim were princes or nobility (Onkelos, Bereshith Rabba, Saadya, Targum Jonathan, and Samaritan version). Bishop Ellicott thought that the sons of elohim might be the mighty ones, i.e. Cain's descendants. Stuart Poole thought they were a wicked pre-Adamic race.
3. Genesis, 5. 4.
4. Just as the term 'sons of the prophets' meant prophets . . . those belonging to the school or class of prophets. See also D. W. Robinson, *New Bible Dictionary*, (I.V.F.), p. 1206. Robinson says that the expression may belong to the language of myth. The converse is more probable. It is from this very event that many of the heathen myths have come. We are here dealing with the true origin of the mythical Titans and gods.
5. Dr. Plumptre, in a footnote to the article ANGELS in Smiths *Dictionary of Christian Biography*, Vol. 1. p. 114 says, 'It is clear from quotations in the Fathers that *many* MSS of the LXX rendered the phrase by "angels of god" (August. *De Civ. Dei*, XV 23: Cyril c. Julian ix. p. 296).
6. The angelic 'Watchers' are referred to in Daniel 4. 13, 23.
7. It was adopted by Augustine and Jerome, and so by Knox in the notes to the Roman Catholic Bible.
8. The new edition (1967) of *The Scofield Bible* merely outlines the alternative views on the passage without expressing any conclusion. D. Kidner, *Genesis*, p. 84 says that the Sethite theory defies the normality of language.
9. *Op. cit.*, Vol. 3, p. 512. He adds 'We have here the region of demigods and heroes'.
10. Ovid, *Metam.* 1, 151, speaks of giants before the flood. Sanconiatho (Cory, *Ancient Fragments*, p. 6) speaks of early mortals producing sons of vast bulk and height. Diodorus Siculus Bk. 1. says that the Egyptians believed in giants in the time of Isis and that they warred against Osiris. In Bk. 5. Ch. 3 he records that the inhabitants of Rhodes believed that giants existed before the flood. The first tablet of the Babylonian creation story tells of Lakmu and Lakhamu who became 'mighty' or 'tall' (Heidel's translation) and Anshar and Kishar who were surpassing in stature. Marduk, too, was a giant. Herodotus has a story (1. 67, 68) that Orestes, son of Agamemnon, was seven cubits tall.
11. Possibly from Hebrew 'naphal' to fall, though Skinner I. C. C. *Genesis*, p. 146 does not accept any reference to fallen angels, a view supported however by the Targum of Jonathan and by Rashi. Aquila gives 'those who fall upon' i.e. possibly invaders or conquerors, while Symmachus gives 'the forceful or violent ones'.
12. While in some legends and myths, especially the Norse myths, they are of fabulous size being confused with natural forces like volcanoes and storms, yet there is no need to consider the historical giants as being more than unusually tall. Goliath of Gath was either four cubits and a span, i.e. probably 7 feet 6 inches, according to the Septuagint and Josephus, or six cubits and a span (Hebrew text) which, even at an eighteen inch cubit, would be 9 feet 6 inches and at a 21 inch cubit, nearly 11 feet. Pliny records an Arab named Gabbaras nearly 10 feet tall, Josephus (*Antiquities* 18. 4. 5.) reports a Jew Eleazar 7 cubits tall, i.e. taller than Goliath. There are numerous modern records of men over 8 feet tall. Patrick Ostler, died 1802, was 8 feet 7 inches, J. W. Kelmair, 1887, 8 feet 9 inches and the Russian, Machnow, who came to London in 1905, aged 23, was 9 feet 3 inches. There is a case of a Chinese man who was 8 feet and his sister 8 feet 4 inches. There are no giant races today but among the Watutsi (or

Batutsi) of Ruanda John Gunther (*Meet Central Africa*, p. 79 ff.) says that 15 per cent are giants, some up to 7 feet 6 inches. The king Mwami was 6 feet 9 inches. Heinrich Harrer, *Seven Years in Tibet*, p. 191, notes that the tallest member of the bodyguard of the Dalai Lama was 8 feet.

13. Probably a confused form of the name Japheth.

14. It was only later that Cronus, still carrying his sickle, became Chronos the god of Time.

15. For a dramatic study of the effects of the confusion of languages see the fascinating work of fiction by C. S. Lewis, *That Hideous Strength*.

CHAPTER 6

NOAH AND THE ARK

IN the midst of such moral decline and violence God spoke to one man—Noah.[1] That God communicated directly with him is asserted seven times.[2] The fact lingers in a number of heathen accounts. In the version preserved by Berossus, Cronus appeared to Xisuthros in a dream and spoke to him, while in the Gilgamesh epic Ea commanded Ut-napishtim to build an ark. In the more confused Indian story Vishnu, disguised as a fish, spoke to Satyavrata about a coming flood, and a similar divine warning is mentioned in many North and South American Indian Flood stories.

To those who believe in God at all there is no difficulty in believing that God could and would communicate with man. The Bible, from first to last, constantly asserts that this is so. Moreover the rest of the Bible indicates that God constantly gives warnings of judgment to come and time for repentance. Thus the story here is exactly in line with the rest of the Bible: God not only speaks to Noah but allows the whole period of the construction of the ark as a time for human repentance.

If we press the question a little further and ask how God speaks to men, the Bible provides an answer. In some cases God speaks to people in dreams (e.g. Pharaoh, Nebuchadnezzar), to others in visions (e.g. Isaiah, Ezekiel, Daniel), and to others by a voice which they hear (e.g. Samuel, Saul of Tarsus, John the apostle on Patmos). In the case of Moses God not only spoke to him but clearly showed him a vision or 'pattern' of the Tabernacle.[3] We may conclude that Noah heard a voice telling him what to do and giving him the dimensions of the great structure which he was to make, and it is quite possible that God revealed or showed to him in a vision the type of vessel required, just as He gave to Moses the pattern of the Tabernacle. And if some, looking at things from a more human standpoint, would assert that down the centuries many men and women have been convinced that they have heard an inner voice telling them to do something, and they have obeyed, this we do not deny. And if they would add that many a great architect or engineer has closed his eyes and seen clearly in his mind some vast cathedral or bridge or ocean liner that with infinite care and pains he has afterwards drawn and finally seen constructed—all this we gladly admit. It is not possible for us with our limited human knowledge to draw some line between what arises in the mind of a creative genius and what use the guiding power of God makes of the gifts He has given to men. What we do assert is that by some means God conveyed to Noah both the pattern and the dimensions of the Ark. It seems reasonable also, on the natural level, to suppose that Noah possessed that constructive genius which manifests itself from time to time throughout history in the construction of something far beyond the achievement of a man's contemporaries. It was surely the type of genius shown by Imhotep in the design of the Step Pyramid, by the architect of the Hanging Gardens of Babylon, by Ictinus and Callicrates in the building of the Parthenon and by Chares of Lindus in the construction of the Colossus of Rhodes, or to come nearer to our own times by Isambard Kingdom Brunel in his ships the *Great Britain* and the *Great Eastern*. Had Noah's Ark remained for mediaeval and modern experts to study it would have been hailed for what it must in fact have really been, the first of the more than seven wonders of the ancient world. If we reject the story and say that the task was too great and that no man could have stood out so far ahead of his contemporaries then we must needs reject the other seven wonders of the ancient world. Noah was only the first of that line of geniuses who designed and constructed something which far outshone the capacity of their contemporaries.

Before we consider in detail the dimensions, structure and

contents of this Ark we must enquire exactly what was required of it. This brings us to the most difficult of all the problems in the study of the Flood. In effect it asks what area of the world was inundated; from what area had Noah to collect the necessary animals. Three main types of answer have been offered. The first, taking the wide general statements of Genesis concerning the 'earth' and the 'whole heaven' in our MODERN sense of the 'entire planet', maintains that the whole planet was submerged at one time and that Noah took representatives of every kind (though not necessarily every species) of creature, together with adequate food supply for a year, into the Ark. The second view, common to liberal commentaries and to materialistic encyclo-paedias, assumes that the Hebrew account is only a modification of a Sumerian story of a local flood in the Mesopotamian valley requiring the rescue of a few local animals.[4] The third view would be that these answers fail to do justice either to the Bible or to the many facts of geology and archaeology already dis-cussed and would require a great flood covering a much larger area than just the land of the two rivers.

It would seem well to examine the evidence with great care. In Genesis 6 we are told that God spoke to Noah declaring that He would 'bring a flood of waters upon the earth to destroy all flesh wherein is the breath of life from under heaven [and that] everything that is in the earth shall die'. In the earlier sections (Gen. 6. 7, 13) there is a similar warning about the judgment coming upon the human race. In ch. 7. 19–23 we have the fulfil-ment of these . . . 'all the high hills that were under the whole heaven were covered . . . all flesh died that moved upon the earth (ground) . . . all that was in the dry land died . . . every living thing was destroyed which was upon the face of the ground, both man and cattle and creeping thing, and fowl of the heaven'.

These and one or two similar verses seem to demand a univer-sal interpretation. Yet a pause for caution is necessary. What did these words mean to Noah to whom in fact they were spoken? What did they convey to Moses who wrote them? What, in fact, was the 'earth' which Noah knew?

We have grown so used to attaching the meaning 'entire planet' to the word 'earth' that we can hardly conceive of any lesser meaning. But in Hebrew the word *ERETS* by no means always, or even usually, meant the entire planet. Its primary meaning was 'earth' in our sense of 'ground' i.e. solid, rocky, stony or clayey material, and it is only by an extension of its meaning that it comes to mean the 'entire planet'. The study of a Hebrew concordance will prove this and show that the meaning must be determined by the context. In such verses as Genesis 1. 1 'God created the heaven and the earth', Genesis 2. 1 'The heavens and the earth were finished', Genesis 14. 22 'The Most High God, Possessor (probably, Creator) of heaven and earth' the context shows that beyond any doubt the entire planet is intended. But in Genesis 1. 10 'God called the dry land "earth"'— the word is already restricted to two-fifths of the surface of the entire planet, and this by God Himself. In Genesis 2. 11 we meet the word again ' . . . the river which compasses the whole *ERETS* of Havilah' and in v. 13 ' . . . the whole *ERETS* of Ethiopoa'. Now here the context demands a very limited use of the word. It must mean 'land or country'. So, too, we have throughout Genesis the *ERETS* of Nod (Gen. 4. 16), of Shinar (10. 10) Canaan (11. 31) Egypt (13. 10) Philistia (21. 34) and Moriah (22. 2). Again in Genesis 12. 1 Abram is told, 'Get thee out of thy country . . . *ERETS*'. Certainly he was not told to leave the planet! In Genesis 41. 56, 57 the famine of Joseph's day was said to have extended over all the earth, and 'all *ERETS* came to Egypt to buy corn'. Here again the context shows a famine over many lands and many countries coming to Egypt for food but the text does not mean that, for example, the inhabitants of our own islands (who probably built Stonehenge between the times of Abram and Moses) came to Joseph in Egypt for food. All these examples are taken from Genesis—some from chapters before the account of the flood, some from later sections, and the conclusion is inescapable. The word *ERETS* has more often a limited meaning than a universal one. The same conclusion results from a survey of the remainder of the Old Testament. While numerous cases

occur of the word being used for the planet, far more often it
means ground (96 times), land (1476 times) or country (140
times) and even when it sometimes appears to have a universal
meaning this is modified by the context. In Exodus 10. 5, 15 the
locusts of the plague of Egypt are said to 'cover the face of the
earth, that one cannot be able to see the earth . . . (v. 15) they
covered the face of the whole earth . . . ' Plainly the expression
'the whole earth' here does not refer to the entire planet and it
would be completely unfair to the Bible to pretend that it did.
Similarly in Numbers 22. 5, 11 Israel were said to 'cover the
earth' i.e., in fact, the surrounding land. In I Kings 4. 34 and 10.
24 the expression 'all the earth sought Solomon to hear his
wisdom' means people from many lands but would not include
the denizens of tropical forests or inhabitants of remote islands.
Nor did Cyrus mean (II Chron. 36. 23) when he said, 'all the
kingdoms of the earth hath God given me' that he therefore
ruled over Japan or Ireland. And it has often been pointed out
that right into the New Testament we need to keep the same
obvious principle of sound Biblical interpretation when we read
that Caesar Augustus decreed that 'all the world' should be
taxed, for even Augustus did not rule over Scotland or Norway!
The same principle holds for the other expression, Genesis 7. 19,
'all the high hills that were under the whole heaven' were
covered, which at first sight seems to demand a universal interpretation. Yet we have in Deuteronomy 2. 25 an exactly parallel
passage, 'This day will I begin to put the dread of thee and the
fear of thee upon the nations that are under the whole heaven
who shall hear report of thee and tremble because of thee' . . .
plainly referring to all those nations of Canaan and the Middle
East whose inhabitants might have opposed the entrance of
Israel into the Promised Land, but not to every nation throughout the planet.[5]

The Bible speaks of a Flood that annihilated every living thing
—everything that had breath—within that area of the world
known to Noah as 'the whole earth—or land'. If it should be
asserted that such a view of the Flood is merely a concession to

modern geological observations it may be well to point out that
Matthew Poole in his *Synopsis*, (1670), and Bishop Edward
Stillingfleet in his *Origines Sacrae*, (1662), both held that the
Bible did not necessitate a belief that the Flood covered the
entire planet. These books were written 180 years before the real
development of modern geology. In any case we have sought to
establish the position entirely by a comparison of a large number
of scriptures taken in their context.

It is now impossible for us to tell how large an area was included in 'all the land' as Noah knew it. In the early chapters of
Genesis there are hints of a very primitive geography. The land
of the four rivers and lands famed for special minerals are
mentioned. We do not now know what was included in Havilah
and Ethiopia though it is certain that the latter was not the
country which has now taken that name. Even centuries after
the Flood it is doubtful whether the 'known' world would have
reached far beyond Egypt and North India. From some such
area Noah was required to gather specimens of every kind of
cattle and creeping thing and bird—kinds which would have
perished from the earth but for this action. It has never been
fair to the Bible to demand that it teaches that Noah took into
the ark pairs of every species of living creature found over the
entire planet. Although Noah's task was big it was not beyond
his power to carry out.

We may now pause and ask how such a Flood as a sound interpretation of scripture demands, fits in with the geological and
archaeological evidence already discussed. The agreement seems
to be all that could be asked for. We have already shown that the
geological evidence is overwhelming that after the Ice Ages, in
the late Quaternary or Recent period, considerable areas of the
world sank beneath the sea-level and then rose again—some
more than once. These at various times affected the Himalayas,
the Andes, North China, the China Sea, the East Indies, the
coasts of Europe and numerous other places. Some considerable
changes are geologically very recent—some definitely within the
time of Palaeolithic man and some even in Neolithic times.

Among these, and the last of the great ones, was Noah's Flood. Later, much smaller, movements in the same area have been responsible for the clay and silt layers at Ur, Erech and Kish. Some changes were very gradual. Others, like that which engulfed the North Siberian mammoth or piled the heaps of smashed trees in the Arctic, were sudden. Noah's Flood was relatively sudden although the text implies that God gave him a week's warning before the final bursting of the storm. Some of the great earth-movements causing the inundations may have been contemporary, others are scattered over a period of very many centuries. It would seem, even from the evidences of geology and archaeology that the cumulative effect of all these changes, culminating in Noah's Flood, resulted in the extermination of the ancient race—Palaeolithic man.

We are still left with no certain knowledge of the number and types of animals present in the ark. Most of the difficulties disappear at once if we keep to the simple lines of Biblical interpretation set out above. Kangaroos would have had to come a long way from Australia, and as far to return—but if Australia was not part of 'the whole land' known to Noah there was no need for the kangaroo to come. The giraffe would have required a special stall to enable him to stretch his neck—but if Central Africa was not part of the world Noah knew, no problem arises. The mastodon of South America must have made a long journey to reach Sumeria and the giant panda from China would have required a special stock of bamboo shoots for his year's food— but it seems that the Bible does not really require mastodons and giant pandas in the ark. Dogmatism is obviously out of place when we really do not know the answers but it is far more reasonable to suppose that Noah collected—maybe tamed— oxen, sheep, goats, horses, asses, camels, relatives of the deer, animals of the cat, dog, beaver, fox, pig, mole, rat and rabbit tribes, and many birds. Some of the creatures were carnivorous —even the raven! Morris and Whitcomb, in their book on the Flood, favour the idea, possibly derived from Bede, that these hibernated for a year, but this is pure speculation without one shred of evidence. Some carnivores can survive on a partial vegetarian diet and it must be remembered that many of the very small creatures multiply so fast that some could have been available as food. It would also be a speculation, but a very much more reasonable one, to suggest that in many cases Noah would select quite young animals. They would also be tamer and easier to handle as those will know who have brought up animals from their early days. In cases of impending danger, animals, particularly younger ones, look for someone to protect them. We can well believe that with a raging storm outside, and warmth, food, comfort and safety within the Ark the attitude of most of the animals to Noah (even apart from any Divine over-ruling which could certainly have been exercised) would have been that of pets looking to their owners for protection and friendship. It does, however, seem to the present writer that Noah probably found it necessary to include only a small number of the world's carnivores. Most of these creatures lived in far distant lands which were not affected at that time and from which some, like lions, may have gradually migrated with the passing years into Persia, Assyria and even Palestine.

We must be content to remain in ignorance of the exact number of types of animals taken by Noah into the Ark, but following the principles of sound Biblical interpretation outlined above it is quite evident that the number would be perfectly reasonable for Noah to collect and for eight people to care for.[6]

We turn next to a study of this Ark which was to be the means of saving the eight persons mentioned and the assemblage of animals. The word Ark is itself of some considerable interest. While the Babylonian account uses the ordinary word for 'ship' the Hebrew text has the word *TEBAH* which the LXX has rendered *KIBOTOS*. The Hebrew *TEBAH* occurs 26 times in the Genesis account, 15 times in the part usually assigned by the critics to 'P' and 11 in the 'J' sections—evidence, one would have thought, of a single writer and not of two. Further the only other place in the whole Bible where the word occurs is in Exodus 2 (verses 3 and 5) where Moses' mother put him in a little 'ark' among the 'rushes'. Now plainly the great interest which Moses must have had in the story, told him by his mother, of his own preservation from destruction when he was put in a little boat on the water, remained vividly with him when he came to write up the account of that far greater deliverance of his ancestor Noah from the Flood. When he came, therefore, to some archaic word for Noah's great vessel—some word which his readers would probably not even know—he used the far more intelligible word *TEBAH* modelled on the Egyptian word *TEBET*,[7] a chest or box. The Greek *KIBOTOS* of the LXX also means chest or box. We have already seen that in the much distorted Egyptian legend Osiris was put in a *BOX* on the river. The very word itself then provides undeniable evidence that the account is by one author and not two or more, and that that author was well familiar with Egyptian terms. Surely, then, the writer was Moses. Further, even our own English word *ARK* has a long history, for it comes from the Latin *ARCA*, a chest, box or[8] coffin and the verb *ARCEO*, to shut in or protect. It would almost seem that the Latin words are a recollection of some who were protected from danger by being shut in a huge box.

The Ark, so God told Noah, was to be made of gopher wood. Here again we meet matters of interest and uncertainty. The Hebrew word G-Ph-R is never again used in the Bible. Brown, Driver and Briggs in their Hebrew lexicon have no idea of the origin of the word. They venture 'pitch-wood' or 'resin-wood'. The usual suggestions are cypress[9] or cedar, but both of these trees occur elsewhere in the Bible with their ordinary Hebrew names. It has been stated that the Phoenicians used cypress for shipbuilding on account of its lightness and durability, and of the two this wood seems the more likely for the Ark. Again it is quite possible that the Hebrew G-P-R is closely connected with the K-P-R which seems to lie behind *KOPHAR*, pitch and even *KAPHAR* to cover over. Maybe, too, the word K-P-R lies behind *KYPRUS*, Cyprus, and probably our *COPPER*, which word is known to come ultimately from Cyprus via the Latin *CUPRUM*, the metal copper being found in that island whose

G

name is associated with the cypress tree. But, when all is said, it remains true that the word G–P–R is so old that no-one now knows exactly what it meant. The LXX translators merely give 'square timber'. Here again we have evidence that the account which lay before Moses was very old even in his time, and it is possible that he himself did not know the exact meaning of the word but merely transliterated it, thus leaving in Genesis 6 a word which is never again used in the Hebrew Bible.

We are next given the overall dimensions, and a few details of the structure of the Ark, and these we shall examine under three main headings: the total size and capacity of the Ark, the ratios of its dimensions, and the ability of early man to build such a vessel.

The Ark was to be 300 cubits long by 50 cubits wide and 30 cubits high. If we assume the cubit to be about 18 inches[10], the overall dimensions would be 450 feet × 75 feet × 45 feet, giving a total volume, if taken as a rectangular box, of 1,518,750 cubic feet. This, on modern reckoning of gross tonnage for ships, would be equivalent to a vessel of 15,000 tons, but this, of course, is not the actual weight of the vessel. Taking the Ark as being made of cypress wood with planks one foot thick, allowing two extra decks or floors, and reasonable longitudinal and cross walls we can calculate that it would require something like 280,000 cubic feet of timber, which at about 530 oz. per cubic foot gives a dead weight of about 4140 tons. Again if we take ocean water as 35 cubic feet per ton such a vessel completely empty would float with about 4·3 feet below water. To load it to a depth of 15 feet would require 10,000 tons of cargo and to 20 feet 15,000 tons. If now we assumed the weight of the animals as 100 tons and if we allow each animal 20 times its own weight of food and 20 times its weight of water for a year we should have a cargo of 4100 tons. We do not, of course, know how many tons of animals were in the Ark but the above calculation is not unrealistic. We do not know how much water Noah actually carried nor how far he was able to rely on rain—certainly there was plenty of the latter for the first forty days—and surely he who could build such a vessel could have arranged for drainage from its roof. However, we do not know. All we can say is that the figures are completely reasonable and realistic. The supply even of many hundreds of tons of food, perhaps gathered as in the case of Egypt during Joseph's time, over a period of years is by no means fantastic. In fact the early Egyptian records throw a most curious and interesting light on this very question. In the famous Rhind Mathematical Papyrus belonging to early Egyptian times, we have a number of geometrical and arithmetical problems, several of which refer to storing grain in large granaries and to gangs of workmen carrying the grain. From one of these problems it emerges that $3\frac{1}{2}$ hekats of flour could be used to make eighty loaves. It would therefore follow that a hekat of flour would make about twenty-three loaves. Other problems tell of the capacity of granaries—one sixty and another seventy-five 'hundred quadruple hekats'. A little calculation will show that the latter granary held enough grain for $23 \times 4 \times 75 \times 100$ loaves, i.e. 690,000 loaves. This then was the scale on which early Egyptians were prepared to store food. There are in the British Museum very ancient wooden models of some of these granaries. One represents a room estimated as about 60 feet long by 15–16 feet high[11] and not so wide as it is long. The model shows seven bins with holes at the top through which the grain could be poured. These holes were covered with sliding wooden lids, and in the sides of the bins were windows covered with sliding wooden covers from which the grain could be extracted. A flight of wooden stairs leads into the granary and this, together with a little model of a man, suggests that the bins were perhaps 10 feet high. This in fact would allow for men carrying sacks to walk along the top of the bins and tip the grain through the holes in the top. The keeper of the store has a measure for use in dealing out the grain and the names of the types of grain appear on the bins. Some of these models belong to the time of Abraham, about 12th Dynasty, but there is one from the 6th Dynasty which must be very much earlier. There is, then, no difficulty whatever in believing that Noah, who must have been an expert carpenter, could have planned and constructed a number of such rooms or granaries in the Ark. The space between decks in the Ark was about 15 feet—very similar in fact to the height of the Egyptian granaries. The models also show that these early carpenters and joiners could make wooden flights of steps for ascending and descending from floor levels that were about 15 feet apart—just exactly the kind of thing Noah must have had for descending to the lower decks of the Ark. Even the idea of keeping different types of food in separate bins (possibly marked with some sign) so important to Noah with his varying requirements is clearly illustrated by these ancient models. Truly the further one proceeds in the study of Noah and the Ark along simple and sound Biblical principles of interpretation and in the light of scientific and archaeological discoveries the more reasonable does the whole story become.

The Ark was, on any consideration, a very large boat. Some have considered the Biblical figures to be unrealistic and to be beyond the capability of craftsmen of so early a date. Yet there are pictures of boats—one with a steering oar—belonging to predynastic times in Egypt.[12] From the time of Menes, 1st Dynasty, we have a palette with a finely carved picture of a high-prowed boat. It is believed that the very early Egyptians and Phoenicians sailed out over the Mediterranean and there is an account of Pharaoh Snofru[13] (3rd Dynasty) sending forty ships to Byblos to buy cedar wood for shipbuilding. There are references to boats of the Middle Kingdom of Egypt with crews of 120 men. Perhaps the most interesting are the vessels used for transporting giant obelisks down the Nile. An Egyptian official, Ineri, reports that in the time of Thothmes I he had a vessel built for the transport of two obelisks which together weighed about 350 tons. The vessel was about 120 cubits long by 40 cubits wide, i.e. 180 feet by 60 feet. There is a picture of such a vessel in the rock temple of Deir–el–Bahari. But Queen Hatshepsut had a much larger vessel, probably 200 feet by 80 feet designed to transport two great obelisks which weighed 350 tons each. Her boat weighed about 800 tons and with its load 1500 tons. This boat, it will be observed, was wider than the Ark—in fact nearly as wide as the Lusitania.[14] There are on some Cretan gems of 2000 B.C. pictures of ships with sails. These large early vessels were made of very thick smoothed timbers sometimes a foot thick. Such beams were fastened together at regular intervals by special pieces of wood shaped like a letter X

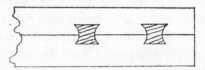

and the joints were then sealed with bitumen. Other members were held by wooden pegs and by such means longitudinal and cross-walls and struts could be inserted and fastened to the main structure.[15] Assuming timbers of about 20 to 30 square feet the whole structure would take from 9000 to 13,000 planks which must have involved cutting down a large number of trees. But we must remember that the story itself seems to suggest that Noah took many years to build the Ark. And once again the task is not nearly so incredible as it first appears. In an interesting little booklet, *The Neolithic Revolution* by Sonia Cole, we have a picture of a Danish workman cutting down a tree with a Neolithic polished stone axe. Three workmen cleared 600 square yards of birch forest in 4 hours using these tools, and a stone-age axe which had not been sharpened for 4000 years was used to fell 100 trees.[16] Besides the axe, early man used the adze for smoothing his beams and saws for cutting. The British Museum has a Badarian (i.e. Pre-Dynastic) flint saw which still looks very efficient. It is known that in Egypt copper was used alongside stone almost back to the beginning of the Neolithic period and the Bible certainly claims that metals had been discovered just before the Flood. Tubal-cain, we are told, was 'the instructor of every artificer in bronze and iron'.[17] These quaint, early expressions like that which calls Jabal 'the father of those that dwell in tents' and Jubal 'the father of all who handle the harp and pipe' seem to be an archaic way of saying that the person concerned was in the first case the inventor of tents, in the second case of musical instruments and in the third case that Tubal-cain was the pioneer in metallurgy. What he discovered and how far his discovery spread we do not now know, but it seems probable that in a small local area of the world the use of copper was discovered before the Flood. It would seem possible that Noah and those who helped him might have had some copper tools. Thus, with axes, adzes, saws and drills[18] either of copper or stone, or both, Noah and his workmen would have had no more difficulty in shipbuilding than had the early Egyptians or Phoenicians.

Yet even granting all this some may feel that the Ark was too large for early man to have attempted. A survey of the ancient world shows in fact the very reverse. One is constantly amazed at the enormous tasks which our ancestors attempted. The Great Pyramid was not the work of the later Pharaohs; it was the work of the 4th Dynasty—long before Abraham! This pyramid contained over two million blocks of stone each weighing about $2\frac{1}{2}$ tons. Its vast sides, 756 feet long,[19] are set to the points of the compass to an accuracy of a small fraction of one degree! The so-called Colossi of Memnon again are not of recent times—they belong to the 18th Dynasty of Egypt. Cut from blocks of sandstone they weigh 400 tons each and were brought 600 miles to their present position. Among the remains of that most ancient Empire in Greece—Mycenae—is the 'Treasury of Atreus'. Above its entrance rests a huge stone lintel 28 feet across. It weighs 120 tons! The Temple of Jupiter at Baalbek is later, but it is staggering to find in the retaining wall three great blocks of stone each weighing about 700 tons. In a quarry nearby is a partly cut block that would have weighed 1000 tons! As our thoughts go back to the Colossus of Rhodes, the Pharos Lighthouse,[20] the Hanging Gardens, the Ziggurats, the Step Pyramid —or even in our own land, to Stonehenge[21]—we have no reason to suppose that early man was afraid to tackle great tasks.

To look at this same question again in a somewhat different light we can find in modern times an example of a tremendous

leap in shipbuilding by a single designer. In 1853 the largest
vessel of her type in the world was the P. & O. liner *Himalaya*,
240 feet by 35 feet with a tonnage of 3438 gross. Yet at the same
time Isambard K. Brunel was planning, and in 1858 produced,
the *Leviathan*, later called the *Great Eastern*, 692 feet by 83 feet
by 30 feet of approximately 19,000 tons . . . five times the tonnage of any ship then afloat. So vast was Brunel's leap that even
forty years later in an age of fierce competition the largest liners
being built were still smaller than the *Great Eastern*.[22]

The Ark was, according to the specifications laid down, to be
300 cubits long by 50 cubits wide by 30 cubits high. The ratios
of these numbers are very interesting. They obviously reflect an
advanced knowledge of shipbuilding. The Babylonian account
which speaks of the Ark as a cube betrays complete ignorance.[23]
Such a vessel would spin slowly round. But the Biblical ratios
leave nothing to be desired.[24] These ratios are important from
the point of view of stability, of pitching and of rolling. The ratio
of length to breadth, 300 to 50 is 6 to 1. Taking the mean of six
present-day ships of approximately the same size, selected from
six different shipping lines, we obtain, as an example, a ratio of
8·1 to 1. The giant liner *Queen Elizabeth* has a ratio 8·6 to 1 while
the Canberra has 8·2 to 1. But these vessels were designed for
speed; the ark was not. Some of the giant tankers have ratios
around 7 to 1. Still more interesting are the figures for the *Great
Britain* designed by I. K. Brunel in 1844. Her dimensions were
322 feet by 51 feet by 32½ feet so that the ratios are almost
exactly those of the Ark. Brunel had the accumulated knowledge
of generations of shipbuilders to draw upon. The Ark was the
first of its kind!

The height of the Ark, 45 feet, was to be divided into three
storeys[25] or decks giving an average of 14 feet each if we allow
for the thickness of the floors and assume only a slight slope on
the roof. The Ark was also evidently divided longways and cross-
ways into compartments or bulkheads. The AV speaks of 'rooms'
which Knox calls 'cabins'. It would be reasonable to assume at
least two long dividing walls running the length of the ship

making a central passage with rooms on either side. The Babylonian account suggests nine cross-walls, but as it also claims six decks and a cubic overall shape, this number, while possibly based on some tradition, is not to be taken as certain. It will be seen, however, that with a central passage of 15 feet the side rooms could be about 30 feet wide, and if there were 9 divisions giving 10 rooms in the 450 feet length each would be 45 feet. We have, of course, no real idea as to how Noah planned out these rooms which were probably not all equal in size, but the average of 20 rooms, 30 feet × 45 feet, on each floor gives some indication of the space available to him. These walls would, of course, give the necessary strength to the whole structure, a fact to which Josephus seems to refer in his account.[26]

There would be doors of some kind to these rooms in addition to the main door of the Ark which we are told was in its side.[27] We have already seen from the very early Egyptian granaries that there was no difficulty in constructing a flight of wooden steps 15 feet high, so that Noah and his family could easily go from one deck to another. A sloping ramp would have been equally easy for Noah to construct if it were required for moving animals from one deck to another.

One important detail in the text has occasioned some difficulty in translation and interpretation—the 'window'. That all living creatures in the Ark would require air and light is obvious, and while the Babylonian account quite overlooks this the Bible makes provision for both. The Hebrew text of Genesis 6. 16 as translated in the AV reads: 'A window shalt thou make to the ark and in a cubit shalt thou finish it above'. The word used here for window, *TSOHAR*, is never again used in this sense in the Old Testament, and it is quite different from the word *CHALLON* used in Genesis 8. 6 where Noah opened 'the window which he had made' to release the birds. It is also different from the word *ARUBBAH* used in Genesis 7. 11 for the 'windows of heaven'. Obviously this unusual word *TSOHAR* requires further investigation. Brown, Driver and Briggs[28] give the word as meaning 'noon' but later[29] they say that they prefer the meaning 'roof' to 'light' in Genesis 6. 16 although admitting that the latter is a possible translation. Now the word comes from a root meaning to 'mount (in the sky) mid-day, or to shine'. Its cognates mean 'glitter, glisten or shine', and one similar word means 'oil' which is used to give light or to make things shine. The fact that it is equivalent to an Assyrian word for 'back' or even 'roof' seems of less importance—despite Brown, Driver and Briggs. But surely conclusive is the fact that on every one of the other 23 occasions in the Old Testament where *TSOHAR* occurs it means noon, mid-day. The word plainly means light, as of the mid-day sun, and is given by other authorities as 'brilliance'. Dean Alford[30] translates the passage 'Light shalt thou make for the ark'. As there was no glass available in such early times it is obvious that this space was open and would admit air. Thus God made provision for light and air, two essentials for the living creatures in the ark. If these living creatures—including Noah and his family—being the lightest part of the cargo[31] were on the top deck or floor, then the window would have to provide light and air for the greater part of the length of the top deck.[32] It would seem that the 'window' or 'light' was an open space running possibly nearly the full length of both sides just below the roof which would doubtless be slightly sloping and overhang by a sufficient amount for the rain to fall clear of the walls. This space or light may have been a cubit in height or possibly the text means that the roof was a cubit above the windows: the meaning of the verse is uncertain.[33] The 'window' would be divided at intervals by the main beams either of the cross-walls or of additional 'ribs' used to strengthen the whole structure. The 'light' would, in fact, consist of many rectangular windows. These could be closed by sliding wooden panels in exactly the same way that we have already seen that the apertures of the granaries were closed. Further, those which came opposite any rooms in which birds were housed would require a lighter, open, lattice work to prevent the escape of these creatures and it is for this reason that the writer in Genesis 8. 6 uses the other word, which in the Old Testament always means a lattice type window. Such a lattice, as we see from Old Testament references, could be slid aside or opened, just as we are told Noah did, for the release of birds.

The arrangements within the Ark seem to be as follows. Noah, his family and the living creatures—a total weight maybe of a hundred or so tons—lived on the top floor where there was ample provision of light and air, and with provision for closing the window spaces when necessary. On the two lower decks the food and water for these creatures, perhaps weighing some thousands of tons, was stored in bins or containers. Thus by far the greater part of the weight was well down in the hold as would be required in the safe loading of any ship and once again we can only marvel at the care and design revealed by the Biblical account of the Ark when contrasted with the crude cubic vessel of the Gilgamesh Epic. There can be no doubt as to which is the original, first-hand description!

The Ark, when completed, was to be rendered waterproof and to achieve this Noah was commanded to 'pitch it within and without with pitch'. The English version here preserves that similarity of verb and noun which is often found in the early chapters of Genesis.[34] In this particular case the words might be given as '*KAPHAR* it within and without with *KOPHER*'. That the two words are closely related and from a common root it would be impossible to deny, but that they have since acquired new meanings is equally true. The primary meaning of *KAPHAR* is 'to cover or hide'[35] and from this it came to be applied to covering with such materials as pitch, and also to cover in a moral sense, i.e. to cover over sin, hence to atone.[36] Thus this word, which only once in the Old Testament means to cover with bitumen, everywhere else means to atone, to reconcile or to forgive. In like manner the word *KOPHER*, which in Genesis 6. 14, and there only, means pitch or bitumen, everywhere else signifies a ransom, or a means of making atonement or obtaining satisfaction. Brown, Driver and Briggs[37] relate the word to the Assyrian *KUPUR* which is reasonable enough, and the LXX renders the passage 'Thou shalt asphalt

it with asphalt'. The material known to the Assyrians as
KUPUR or *KUPRU* and to the Greeks as asphalt is the bitu-
minous substance found in the oil-bearing regions around the
ancient crescent from the Dead Sea (Lake Asphaltitis) to Persia.
Whilst it varies in nature it is the heavy black substance, sometimes solid, sometimes a viscous liquid, associated with the
petroleum-bearing regions. In Roman times[38] great lumps of it
used to float on the Dead Sea. The substance, which was ideal
for rendering ships waterproof, was found in great quantities in
Babylonia.[39] Large amounts came from Hît or Id, a place only
ninety miles from Baghdad, and hence probably near to the place
where Noah constructed the ark. Some of the earliest references
to bitumen are very interesting, especially in our present study.
'The steward of the Gods, Gudea, King of Lagash' about 2400
B.C. obtained supplies of bitumen from the mountains of
Magda. A quantity of 110 tons is mentioned. In other similar
documents we read of 7 tons and of 56 tons of bitumen.
Another ancient record quotes the price, $3\frac{1}{2}$ shekels of silver
per ton. One defeated city had to pay 290 tons as tribute to
the king of Ur, and yet another record speaks of five shiploads
of bitumen. Certainly Noah would have had no difficulty in
obtaining adequate supplies for the Ark. Strabo says that bitumen was obtained from Hît and that it was used to make boats
impervious to water. In shipbuilding it was 'filled' or reinforced with chopped straw, rushes or reeds, sometimes up to 15
per cent.

The Bible gives no clue as to the amount that Noah would have
required, but the Babylonian version of the Gilgamesh Epic[40]
says: 'Six sar (measures) of bitumen I poured into the furnace,
three sar of asphalt I poured inside, three sar of oil the basket-
bearers carried'.

The exact meaning of the passage is not clear but Pritchard
says that each 'sar' may represent 8000 gallons, giving 48,000
gallons. Calculation shows that this would have been enough to
cover the outside and inside shell of the Ark completely with
bitumen half an inch thick, or somewhat less if the roof was also

coated. The actual thickness would be less because some would be forced into cracks and crevices and some would soak into the timbers. The Ark, then, was rendered waterproof by the use of materials easily available in large quantities in the very region where it was most likely constructed.

NOTES

1. The name Noah was given by Lamech (Gen. 5. 29) 'saying, This one shall comfort (or rest) us from our toil'. The Hebrew Nacham = to comfort, Nuach = to rest. The name is said to occur in Mari and other Hurrian texts as the name of a god. Black's *Bible Dictionary*, p. 199.
2. Genesis 6. 13 ; 7. 1 ; 8. 15 ; 9. 1, 8, 12, 17.
3. Exodus 25. 40 ; Hebrews 8. 5. The Hebrew for 'showed' is the ordinary word for 'to cause to see'.
4. This is the strangely inadequate conclusion of H. Peake, *The Flood*, (1930), p. 111. 'The Flood came about 4250 B.C. This destroyed the villages and reed huts of the earlier people, and drowned all their inhabitants except the headman of the village of Shuruppak and his family. This man, Xisuthros, Uta-Napishtim or Noah, had been warned, so Woolley thinks, by a friendly Sumerian, and had built a boat in which he and his companions escaped. The whole valley was now free for the Sumerians, who had escaped destruction by taking refuge in their elevated cities, protected as they were by brick walls. These people soon took possession of the whole land.'
5. This is absolutely confirmed by Moses' own interpretation of God's promise in Deuteronomy 11. 25 where he says: 'The Lord your God shall lay the fear of you and the dread of you upon all the land that ye shall tread upon, as He hath said unto you'. Thus Moses interprets 'under the whole heaven' of the promise as every land through which Israel passed. Commenting on the same expressions Prof. A. Rendle Short *Modern Discovery and the Bible*, (1949), pp. 135, 136, says, 'Words in the Bible, as in any other old book, are used in the sense that they bore at the time of writing, and not in the sense that they have come to bear today. It was the then-known world that went under the Deluge and the then-known animals that were preserved alive'. That great evangelical scholar, the late E. F. Kevan (I.V.F. *Bible Commentary*, (1953), p. 84) says, 'The universal terms must be understood in the light of their context'—and quotes Genesis 41. 57 ; Deut. 2. 25 ; I Kings 10. 24 ; Rom. 1. 8 ; 10. 18 as proof. Bernard Ramm, *The Christian View of Science and Scripture*, pp. 150–163 and D. Kidner, *Genesis*, pp. 94, 95 both interpret this section of Genesis as referring to the then known 'earth'.
6. Authorities are divided on the meaning of Genesis 7. 2, 'Of every clean beast thou shalt take to thee by sevens, the male and his female'. J. Hellmuth, *Biblical Thesaurus, Genesis*, translates the Hebrew as 'seven seven' and adds, 'i.e. seven couples'. *The Speaker's Commentary* gives 'seven pairs' and Dean Alford agrees. J. Skinner, *Genesis*, p. 152, says 'seven individuals rather than seven pairs', but he mentions that the Midrash, Bereshith Rabba and Ibn Ezra prefer 'pairs'. Morris and Whitcomb are definite for seven individuals, quoting Hebrew authorities in support of this view. E. F. Kevan, *New Bible Dictionary*, says 'this might mean seven pairs but more probably three pairs and an additional one for an offering'. In any case it is absurd to say, as some of the critics have said, that this passage contradicts the other verses which speak of

animals going by twos and that therefore this verse was written by a different author.

7. How comes it, on the Higher Critical theory, that a Hebrew writer uses an Egyptian word in an account supposedly borrowed from the Babylonians?
8. As the Ark of the Covenant was also a rectangular box the English versions have used the same word *ARK*—but the Hebrew word in this case (*ARON*) is quite different.
9. The Targum here has cypress. W. H. Rule, *Oriental Records*, p. 24.
10. D. J. Wiseman, *New Bible Dictionary*, I.V.F., gives 17·5 inches for the ordinary Hebrew cubit. The Siloam tunnel is described in the original inscription as 1200 cubits long and it is in fact 1750 feet. The Babylonian cubit was 19·8 inches and the Indus Valley seems to have had a 20·6 inch cubit similar to the royal cubit of Ezekiel 40.
11. A great granary was found at Harappa in N. India belonging to the period 2500–1500 B.C. It stood on a raised platform 150 feet by 200 feet and was divided into storage rooms 50 feet × 20 feet. Close by there were brick floors in the centre of which had stood great wooden mortars where the grain was pounded by heavy wooden pestles. Remains of different types of grain were actually found. This, and the evidence from Egypt, shows that early man was quite used to storing vast quantities of food. For a description of the astonishing civilizations of Harappa and Mohenjo Daro, in the Indus valley, civilizations evidently developed by the early descendants of Noah, see A. L. Basham, *The Wonder that was India*, (London 1954), and Stuart Piggott, *Prehistoric India*, (London 1950).
12. There is a pot in the Cairo Museum on which is depicted a large boat with two animals sketched above it. This belongs to the Gerzean period—i.e. before the First Dynasty of Egypt. See *Encyclopedia of Prehistoric Art*, René Huyghe, (1957), p. 62, Fig. 72. The 'Uruk' Cylinder, sometimes dated 3000 B.C., shows men and animals on a boat and has been considered by some to refer to Noah. E. Anati, *Palestine before the Hebrews*, p. 19, has a copy of a very early Egyptian rock-carving showing an Asiatic type of boat in which are five human figures, two large and three small.
13. Some of Snofru's achievements are recorded on the Palermo Stone. In the thirteenth year of his reign a great ship of 100 cubits length was built as well as 60 lesser ships. In the fourteenth year another cedar ship of 100 cubits was built. See *A History of Egypt*, W. M. Flinders Petrie, Vol. 1. p. 34. (1903 Edition).
14. These may be referred to in the Gilgamesh Epic, Tablet XI, 1. 63 which Pritchard translates: 'I hammered water-plugs into her'. The British Museum (1920) translation gives 'water bolts' as being driven into the vessel. For additional details of early shipbuilding see *The Ship* by Björn Landström, (1961).
15. Dowels and pegs can be found in 1st Dynasty and even earlier, Egyptian woodwork. Lucas, *Ancient Egyptian Materials*, p. 513 gives mortise and tenon joints and dove-tailing at least as early as 4th Dynasty. Planks were smoothed with pieces of fine-grained sandstone.
16. The oldest known polished stone axes come from the Caspian Sea region. C. S. Coon, *The History of Man*, p. 82. North American Indians were able to make cedar planks using stone tools.
17. The word instructor is better translated 'forger' (RV) or polisher (Alford). Jewish tradition (Bereshith Rabba) says that Naamah, the sister of Tubal-Cain, was Noah's wife. This would raise questions of great interest. Some have suggested that Tubal-Cain is the original of Vulcan or Hephaistos, Naamah (=lovely) of Venus. If Naamah was the wife of Noah it would mean that Noah, being related to Tubal-Cain, would have access to metal tools. It would also mean that Shem, Ham and Japheth came of the Sethite line through their father and the Cainite line through their mother. But nothing can be deduced for certain from Jewish

tradition. Late Jewish tradition says that Shem, Ham and Japheth married the daughters of Eliakim son of Methuselah but this also is of course without any real foundation.

18. Copper saws up to 16 inches long are known from the 1st Dynasty of Egypt. A. Lucas, *Ancient Egyptian Materials*, p. 510.

19. The difference between the longest side and the shortest side of the Great Pyramid is 8 inches—the sides are 756 feet long, so that the maximum error is 8 in 9072 or 0·09 per cent. The maximum error in direction is 5′ 30″ on the east side, an eleventh of a degree!

20. The Pharos lighthouse was 400 feet high.

21. The large blocks at Stonehenge weigh 50 tons.

22. For example the crack Cunard Liners Campania and Lucania (1893) were 13,000 tons and the German Kaiser Wilhelm der Grosse (1897) 14,350 tons. The 36 ton propeller of the Great Eastern remains the largest single propellor ever cast. There has been a similar leap in our own times. In 1960 the largest tankers were of about 80,000 tons; by 1968 the Japanese had built a 312,000 ton tanker. A Tyneside firm speaks of building vessels of 1,000,000 tons.

23. Berossus gives the ratio of length to breadth as 5 to 2 i.e. 2½ to 1.

24. In 1604 a Dutch merchant, Peter Jansen, had a boat built at Hoorn, 120 feet × 20 feet × 12 feet i.e. exactly the same ratios as the Ark. The vessel proved to be admirably suited for carrying freight. It is said that several vessels with the same proportions were built in Denmark.

25. The suggestion (*New Bible Dictionary*, Article 'Ark') that this might possibly mean 'three layers of logs laid cross-wise' is most unlikely. This would leave the Ark a great empty box 45 feet high inside! The decks and cross-walls were obviously essential to make the 'rooms' and also to give rigidity to the whole structure. In the Babylonian account the Ark had six storeys.

26. 'Now this ark had firm walls and a roof, and was braced with cross beams'. Josephus, *Antiquities* I. 3. 2.

27. Snofru speaks of making great cedar doors for his palace in his fourteenth year. W. Flinders Petrie, *History of Egypt*, Vol. I. p. 34.

28. F. Brown, S. R. Driver and C. A. Briggs, *Hebrew and English Lexicon*, p. 843.

29. *Ibid.*, p. 844.

30. H. Alford, *Genesis*, p. 32.

31. See p. 88.

32. A later Jewish work *Pirqe Rabbi Eliezer*, probably ninth Century A.D. puts all the beasts on the lowest floor, the birds on the middle and creeping things and Noah's family on the upper deck.

33. For the subsequent curious history of the 'light' in the Ark see Appendix I.

34. See, for example, Chapters 12 and 14 of the author's *Creation Revealed*.

35. Brown, Driver and Briggs, *Hebrew Lexicon*, p. 497.

36. *Ibid.*

37. *Ibid.*, p. 498.

38. Diodorus Siculus, Bk. 19. Ch. 6.

39. Sargon of Akkad, who must be dated well before the first dynasty of Babylon, was said to have been put as a babe into the river in a basket of rushes coated with bitumen. R. W. Rogers, *Cuneiform Parallels to the Old Testament*, p. 135.

40. J. B. Pritchard, *The Ancient Near East*, p. 67.

CHAPTER 7

THE DELUGE, THE DOVE AND THE DELIVERANCE

'NOAH did', so the simple, very straightforward, account of Genesis 6. 22 tells us, 'according to all that God commanded him, so did he'.[1] Seven days before the actual bursting of the Flood (Genesis 7. 4, 10) God warned Noah to complete all preparations and on the seventeenth day of the second month in Noah's 600th year the Deluge commenced.[2]

Once again some most intriguing problems come before us as we consider Noah's calendar. We shall look at the year stated and then at the day and the month. The great ages of the patriarchs have always been a problem. Do these figures like 600 and 900 represent actual ages in years of 365 days or not? Four lines of answer have been proposed. The years, according to some, were just our months—or moons—and the total should be divided by twelve. This we reject completely, as not only can it be shown to be absolutely wrong, but it makes more difficulties than it solves. Enoch, we are told, had a son Methuselah when he was sixty-five. If we divide by twelve he had a son when he was 5·4 years old! The second proposal assumes that the ages are purely mythological and are corruptions from the great ages given to the early kings and heroes in the Babylonian lists. This is an easy way out but the Biblical figures are much more orderly and consistent than the Babylonian, and such a theory does not explain how, in the first place, the idea ever grew up that people before the Deluge lived such long lives. It is at least as likely that the Babylonian figures are the distorted recollection of the actual facts which the Bible correctly records. The third explanation is that the ten 'antediluvian patriarchs' are in fact ten dynasties and that the dates refer to changes in dynasties. This theory is more reasonable and there are, in fact, lists of such dynasties both before and after the Flood and such lists do total up the number of years for each dynasty. On the whole however the theory seems to lack sufficient evidence to make it conclusive. The fourth explanation accepts the figures as they stand and then tries to see what points of interest such a course involves. Certainly the Bible is not alone in asserting that men lived very long lives before the Flood. The Weld-Blundell cylinder 44, for example, allots 28,800 years to Alulim the first king on the list and 18,600 to the last. Berossus, however, according to Abydenus,[3] says that the first king Alorus reigned ten sari, and a sarus is taken to be 3600 years, a neros 600 and a sossus 60. This makes Alorus 36,000 years. Now even if at some stage a confusion has arisen between the sarus at 3600 years and the astronomical cycle known to the later Babylonian astronomers as a saros of 223 lunations or 18 years 11 days, still ten of these would be 180 years. Yet another possible confusion exists in the old Babylonian tablets because of the use of the sexagesimal system and it would seem that in the Weld-Blundell tablet 62 where Ziusudra is credited with 36,000 years the figure is exactly 60 times the Biblical value. For Ziusudra is undoubtedly Noah who has been credited with 10 sari instead of 1 neros.

Another possible, though perhaps less likely, confusion was pointed out by M. Oppert[4] who notes that the Chaldean account allows 432,000 years between Adam and the Flood while the Hebrew reckoning has 1656 years. The Chaldean account is 261 times as long as the Hebrew and 261 is the number of weeks in 5 years. A five year cycle is rare but not unknown in the ancient world but why the number of weeks in it is significant does not appear. The Old Egyptian Chronicle[5] gave to Cronus and 12 other kings a total of 3984 years and Manetho allowed 724 years for the mythical reign of Hephaestus although he allotted reasonable figures for the other predynastic kings. We have already seen that there are recollections of Enoch among races as far west as the Aztecs[6] who credit him with an age of 300. Josephus[7] claims that besides Manetho and Berossus numerous other ancient writers, including Mochus, Hestiaeus, Hieronymus the Egyptian, Hesiod, Hellanicus, Acusilaus, Ephorus and Nicolaus, agreed that early men lived nearly a thousand years. There is, then, a strong tradition outside the Bible as well as within it that people before the Flood enjoyed much longer lives than they now do. But if this was so it raises a number of curious problems to which we at present have no answer. Certainly the present life-span of man is not long enough to allow him to enjoy the fruits and to make use of the timber of a number of trees which he plants, but must leave to the next generation to enter into. The causes of ageing and death are still very little known. Man has obviously introduced many harmful factors into his own life by war, murder, dirt, ignorance, insanitary conditions and wrong use of drugs and natural products. Bacteria and viruses do not seem to be getting less despite the progress made in exterminating some of them. But we know still less about the subtle effects such as those of cosmic rays on the human life span, although we do know that they are responsible for the presence of the small amount of radio-carbon in the atmosphere and hence in our own bodies, and also that rays and radio-active substances can cause irreversible damage to living cells. It has been suggested that before the Flood the cosmic ray activity at the surface of the Earth was much lower and this might account for greater longevity as well as making all radio-carbon dates appear to be higher than they should. But all this is no more than speculation and interesting though it may be we must leave it with the confession that at present we do not know the answer.

The passage in Genesis informs us that the Deluge commenced on the seventeenth day of the second month. A few years ago it would have been emphatically declared by some critics that no such calendar could have existed so far back in human history as the times assigned to Noah. Yet we now know that very early man was a keen watcher of the skies. Not only did men of the first dynasties of Babylon keep accurate measurements not

H

merely of months but of the position of a planet like Venus[8] but far earlier than this men observed a calendar sequence. Alexander Marshack has shown[9] from the study of hundreds of markings made by Palaeolithic men on walls of caves, on bones and on pieces of ivory—even mammoth ivory—that early men marked off the days of the months as they passed. Some even noted the four quarters of the moon. These calendars go back to Magdalenian and Aurignacian times. The method of recording days by notches on sticks still persists to this day among primitive people. Even more interesting is the fact that the Babylonian account of the Flood actually asserts that Noah kept a calendar by marking off the days on the wall, for in the 10th Tablet (lines 209–212), when Gilgamesh was asleep, Utnapishtim said to his wife, 'Up, bake for him wafers . . . and mark on the wall the days he sleeps . . . she baked him wafers . . . and marked on the wall the days he slept'. Gilgamesh apparently slept for a week!

We can thus conclude that Noah kept his calendar by marking the days on the wall of the Ark. From the number of times that the figure seven is mentioned it would appear that he kept some kind of sabbath sequence, but from the fact that no stress is laid on this it would appear that the account was probably written before the special inauguration of the keeping of the sabbath at the time of the Exodus.

In very ancient calendars the months had no names—they were simply numbered—but as time went on names, either of gods or of seasons, were attached to them. In the case of the Hebrew calendar it must always be remembered that the starting point was changed by Divine decree at the Exodus when the seventh month became the 'first month of the year'.[10] All Hebrew dates, then, from the Exodus to the Captivity differ by six months from the old reckoning. The Babylonians retained the old calendar and the Jews at the Captivity in Babylon reverted to the old system and down to this day keep their New Year in September and not in March. Remembering that in early times the months had only numbers and not names we can set out Noah's calendar and compare it with later reckonings.

Events	No. of month in Old Calendar	Later names	No. of month after Exodus	Macedonian name and order		Approximate modern equivalent
Waters dried 1/1/601	1	Tishri	7	Hyperbereteus	12	Sept.–Oct.
Flood commenced 17/2/600, „ ends 27/2/601	2	Marcheswan Bul	8	Dius	1	Oct.–Nov.
40 days 26/3/600	3	Kislev	9	Apellaeus	2	Nov.–Dec.
	4	Tebeth	10	Audynaeus	3	Dec.–Jan.
	5	Shebat	11	Peritius	4	Jan.–Feb.
	6	Adar	12	Dystrus	5	Feb.–March
Ark rests 17/7/600 after 150 days	7	Nisan, Abib	1	Xanthicus	6	March–April
	8	Iyar, Ziph	2	Artemesius	7	April–May
	9	Sivan	3	Daesius	8	May–June
Tops of mountains seen 1/10/600	10	Tammuz	4	Panemus	9	June–July
40 days to 10/11/600 Birds released	11	Ab	5	Lous	10	July–Aug.
	12	Elul	6	Gorpiaeus	11	Aug.–Sept.

The length of Noah's months is not absolutely certain. The account says that the Flood started on 17/2/600 and that the waters prevailed for 150 days, during the latter part of which they were 'returning from off the earth'. After this the Ark rested on 17/7/600. If all Noah's months had 30 days and we include the day on which the Flood started and also the sixteenth of Nisan, but not the actual day on which the Ark rested, we shall have $14 + 30 + 30 + 30 + 30 + 16 = 150$, and this seems the most likely as the word 'after' seems to exclude the seventeenth Nisan itself from the 150. If, on the other hand, Noah included, as later Hebrew chronologists did, both the initial and final days we can only obtain 150 by making one of the months 29 days, thus $14 + 30 + 29 + 30 + 30 + 17 = 150$. This implies a very unusual calendar, yet strangely enough there was an ancient Chinese calendar which read 30, 30, 29, 30, 30, 29, 29, 30, 29, 29, 30, 29 days. But the former alternative of 30-day months seems more likely and suggests that Noah was working to a fixed calendar and not by observation of the moon. We cannot deduce from his dates whether this calendar had any intercalary period.

We come now to the actual dates as recorded. Probably few people have realized the amazing facts which lie behind these dates. The Flood commenced on the seventeenth day of the second month, i.e. the month later known as Marcheswan.[11] This month ran from a date (which could vary) in October to one in November. Taking the average date for the commencement of one of Noah's months as about the middle of one of our months the Flood must have started early in November. When at last the Flood had completely receded and Noah emerged from the Ark the date is recorded as the twenty-seventh day of the second month of the following year. Thus the old world perished in November and a year later a new era commenced in the same month. Both of these facts are indelibly enshrined in the memory of the human race. To many people right round the world November brings the Day of the Dead. In a number of ancient and primitive calendars November also brings a New Year at a time which has neither solstice nor equinox nor astronomical event to justify it.

November 2 is All Souls' Day—the Day of the Dead. In France it is Le Jour des Morts—christianized now for centuries but still at heart the Old Day of the Dead when flowers are taken to the tombs. From South America to Northern Europe, from Mexico to Polynesia gifts and flowers are placed on tombs on this anniversary of the Day of Death. The ritual has in some cases been absorbed into, or modified by, later religions but the recollection of that Day of Judgment and Death has never ceased. It has long been known that the ship of Isis and the chest or coffin of Osiris which floated on the waters for a year are confused Egyptian recollections of the Flood.[12] Plutarch says that Osiris was shut up in his box and set afloat 'on the seventeenth day of the month Athyr, when the nights were growing long and the day decreasing'.[13] Now the Egyptian months had no names in very early times, only numbers, and their months shifted through the year owing to the omission of leap years. Plutarch, however, makes it clear that he is referring to the seventeenth day of a month well on in autumn, for the nights were long. In Plutarch's time Athyr did in fact coincide with October–November. In ancient Assyria the ceremonies for the souls of the dead were in the month Arahsamna, which is Marcheswan.[14] In Arahsamna the Sun God became Lord of the Land of the Dead.[15] The month was held sacred to the rain-and-thunder-god, while in Babylon Marduk was called, in connection with this month, 'Lord of the Deep' and also 'Lord of Abundance who causes plenty of rain to fall'. The Hindu 'Durga'—festival of the dead —was originally connected with their New Year which commenced in November. The Persians commenced their New Year in November in a month which was named Mordad-month i.e. the month of the angel of death. In Peru the New Year commenced in November and the festival called Ayamarka— carrying of a corpse—concluded with placing food and drink on graves. The Mexicans, too, kept the Day of the Dead at the same time of the year. Natives in parts of Australia at this time of the year paint white stripes on their legs and arms and ribs to resemble skeletons and the inhabitants of the Society Islands pray for the spirits of departed ancestors at the end of their New Year celebration in November. Our Anglo-Saxon ancestors called November Blood-month! Frazer[16] states that the Celtic inhabitants of our own land—whose traditions incidentally are among the most ancient in the world—kept their New Year in November. The Manx mummers sang, 'Tonight is New Year's night, Hogunnaa'—on Hallowe'en, October 31. Further, November 1 (Old Style) was kept as New Year's day in the Isle of Man until relatively recent times. Frazer sees the ancient Irish custom of kindling fires on Hallowe'en, or the eve of Samhain as showing that November 1 was New Year's day. The Celtic festival of Samhain[17] or Samhnagen held in November is connected with the Cornish New Year festival of Allantide and the Irish Geimredh. In Wales and Scotland early November is the time for ghosts to be remembered. Samhain is connected in legend with Avalon, the kingdom of the Dead, to which Arthur was taken across the waters of a lake.[18]

The Flood commenced and ended in November, lasting just over a year—but the recollection of it has never died out in the memory and the calendars of the descendants of that little group of survivors.

But these amazing facts lead us to something still more wonderful. We are specifically told that after 150 days the Ark rested on the seventeenth day of the seventh month. If the Flood started in November the Ark rested in April, if it started in Marcheswan the Ark rested in Nisan, that month which later became the new first month of the year. The Ark came safely to rest on Nisan 17. Centuries later the Israelites in Egypt took a lamb on Nisan 10, they kept the Passover on Nisan 14 and then set out, pursued by the hosts of Pharaoh, but by the seventeenth everyone was safe across the Red Sea—a new nation, delivered from death and danger. And very many more centuries passed and Christ Himself kept that same Passover memorial and then went, not above, but down into the waters of death to deliver, not eight souls, but an innumerable multitude and then rose triumphant over death itself on Nisan 17. With that Resurrection a new era began, a new creation was commenced.

Thus Christ rose from the dead on the anniversary of the crossing of the Red Sea and the anniversary of the resting of the Ark on the mountains of Ararat. How wonderful indeed was Noah's calendar—or rather God's!

The waters, according to Genesis 8. 5 went down slowly for another two and a half months until on the first day of the tenth month (about June 14) the tops of the surrounding heights could be seen. Noah waited 40 days more—bringing him to about the tenth day of the eleventh month (July 24)—when he opened the lattice window and sent out a raven. It seems that he waited seven days and then sent out a dove but this bird returned to the ark. He waited, (Gen. 8. 10) yet *another* seven days and sent out the dove again. On this occasion it returned with a freshly-plucked olive leaf. He stayed yet one more (v. 12) week and again sent out the dove which this time returned no more. This would bring him to about the beginning of the twelfth month (August 14–15) and after waiting patiently until the end of that month he removed the covering of the Ark and on the first day of the first month of his 601st year (*c.* September 14) he looked out over the surrounding land which was dry. It was not, however, until the twenty-seventh day of the second month that he finally received the command of God to leave the Ark. By this time the surrounding regions, and even more distant lowlands had been dry for some weeks, most of the marshy districts would have become firm and it would be safe to allow the animals to roam at will.

In this part of the story we have, as we have mentioned, a sequence which suggests that Noah observed a seven-day cycle but there is no stressing of the sabbath day.

The recorder of the Flood sees some points of interest in the sending out of the raven and the dove and to these we may now turn.

That Noah sent out birds from the Ark is, of course, asserted by numerous sources besides the Biblical record. Berossus[19] states that Xisuthros sent out birds on three occasions, on one of which they returned with clay on their feet. In the Epic of Gilgamesh[20] Utnapishtim records that after the ship had grounded on Mount Nisir, 'I set free a dove, the dove went forth but came back . . . then I sent forth and set free a swallow, the swallow went forth and came back . . . then I sent forth and set free a raven, the raven went forth and seeing that the waters had diminished he eats, circles, caws and turns not round'. Plutarch[21] says that Deucalion sent out a dove from the ark and when it returned he concluded that the storm was not yet ended but when he saw it no more he knew that the sky was serene again. Some of the ancient medals of Janus (a god who in some aspects reflects the character of Noah) have on one side the heads of Janus and on the other a dove with an olive branch in its mouth.[22] In one Indian legend a goddess, who assumes the form of the ship Argha, after the Deluge flew away as a dove.[23] The Syrian goddess Derceto was supposed to have been born from a floating egg on which was perched a dove.[24] In like manner Venus (who is but a Western form of Derceto) is pictured as rising from the sea attended by her doves. Isis, the Egyptian counterpart of Derceto, was likewise depicted as attended by three doves. There was a strange festival at Eryx in Sicily which Faber[25] connects with the Flood, in which a number of doves were released (the anagogia) one of which was supposed to return to the temple of Aphrodite (the katagogia). The Hindoos have a legend that even the footmark of the dove can still be seen on Mount Chaisa-ghar where Satyavrata's ark came to rest. Various other birds occur in connection with Flood stories as far west as Central and South America.

It is quite clear then, that Noah's experiments in sending out the birds were remembered by his sons and told to succeeding generations, who, in various distorted forms, have remembered them all down history.

Turning to the birds themselves the raven is called in Hebrew *OREB* or *OREV*. There being a slight guttural sound before the O, perhaps in imitation of the raven's call, the name has become in Greek *KORAX* and in Latin *KORVUS*. The name occurs in the book of Judges as that of a prince of Midian *OREB* who was killed at a rock which has since been known as the stone of *OREB*.[26] The place is known to the Arabs as Ush el *GHURAB*. The name has come through to our Norse ancestors as *HRAF* while the B survives in the German *RABE*. Odin was called *HRAFNAGUD*, the Raven God, and he had, as we have mentioned, two ravens Huginn and Munninn which flew abroad every day to gather news for him.[27] The raven is still found associated with memories of the Flood among the North American Indians. The raven is the largest of the crow family,[28] being found from Greenland to India. It will eat almost anything when hungry but prefers carrion and will attack sickly animals up to the size of a sheep although it prefers easier prey. It can live in rocky clefts and often lives near brooks.[29] The subsequent fate of the raven from the Ark is not clear. The text states that 'It went forth, going and returning until the drying of the waters from the earth', but whether this means that it merely flew about, up and down valleys, returning (the same word is used of the dove) to the Ark and maybe perching on it, from time to time, is not certain.[30] It is generally assumed that it did not come back to the Ark and evidently Noah decided to try a different type of bird for his second experiment.

The dove, Hebrew *YONAH* or *JONAH*, is again a well-known bird in the Middle East and as we have seen, common in legend and mythology. Doves or pigeons have always been famous for their ability to undertake long, swift flights and also for their powerful homing instinct. We may reasonably assume that Noah was aware of both these facts. Pigeons have long been used as messengers. They were so used in the days of Solomon.[31] The Romans used them in battles and the Greeks used them to carry the results of the Olympic games.[32] In races they can cover 500 miles in a day. There is tradition among the Greeks[33] that the first olive branch that reached their country was carried by a dove from Phoenicia, to the temple of Zeus in Epirus. Thomson

tells us that olive groves are favourite haunts for doves who
build their nests there and rear their young. Little wonder then
that Noah's dove returned to the ark with 'a freshly plucked
olive leaf'.

It may be well to look a little more closely at this simple statement. Our King James version has 'an olive leaf pluckt off'
while the Revised Version margin has 'a fresh olive leaf' a translation supported by Alford in his commentary. The RSV has
'freshly plucked', and Knox translates the Vulgate as 'with a
twig of olive in its mouth, the leaves still green on it'. It was not,
then, a stray twig that had long floated about but one that had
been still alive and attached to the tree on that very day.

The olive tree (Hebrew *ZAYITH*, Greek *ELAIA*), despite
its modern name *OLEA EUROPAEA*, is believed to have
originated in Western Asia although it spread in very early times
to Greece and the Eastern Mediterranean. There is evidence of
its existence in that part of the world back to Neolithic times. It
existed in Minoan Crete and there is a reference during the 4th
Dynasty of Egypt (period of the great pyramids) to the importing
of olive oil from Palestine and Syria. There was a sacred olive
tree at Heliopolis in the times of the 5th Dynasty.[34] The olive
was known in Persia in very early times and although not now
very common near to Ararat, it is found within the area and
especially near the Caspian Sea and in Afghanistan. It is
mentioned by Homer, and the Greek legend already quoted
that it was brought to the temple of Zeus in Epirus from
Phoenicia by a dove is obviously a faint racial remembrance
of the dove and olive leaf of the Flood. The connection with Zeus
we shall examine below.

The wild olive is a sturdy tree 30–40 feet in height, with
somewhat leathery leaves. It flourishes in fertile regions, likes
chalky soils, often grows near the sea and can attain a great age
and girth. It likes warm climates, cannot long survive below 14°F.
and prefers regions with an average temperature above 50°F.
For this reason it would obviously not grow on the higher parts
of mountains, being generally confined to slopes below 3000

feet. Thus Noah could deduce from the freshly plucked leaf that the lower valleys were becoming free of water. Thomson[35] points out that the Flood could not have covered the area for too long a time or the tree would have been dead, although there is a strange statement attributed to Theophrastus and to Pliny that the olive will grow under water.[36] This may merely be an ancient belief based ultimately on the fact of an olive tree being recorded as surviving the Deluge.

Seeing that the dove brought such good news to Noah by means of the olive leaf it is little wonder that in succeeding centuries the dove and olive branch have become symbols of peace—not so much peace in itself as peace after the storm, peace after conflict.

Quite how much further we can trace the olive in the mists of antiquity it is difficult to say. We have already suggested that Zeus owes something in his legendary beginnings to Ziusudra or Noah. Zeus was not originally a Greek god.[37] In various forms, particularly as the weather-god, the god of rain and storms and thunder, he comes from Western Asia. He is identical with the Sanskrit *DYAUS*, sky, heaven, day, a word which leads to the Latin *DIEM* as well possibly to JOVE[38] and DEOS.[39] But the associations go further. Noah started his new life and world among the mountains of Ararat. Zeus was always associated with a mountain—Olympus. But there were very many mountains which claimed to be Olympus. The name again is *NOT* originally Greek and there were mountains with this name in Asia Minor, in Mysia, Galatia, Lycia, Cilicia,[40] as well as in Cyprus and finally several in Greece, including not only that in Thessaly but the famous centre near to the river Alphaeus. Here by the hill called *KRONION* the Greeks honoured Zeus. Here Phidias constructed his great gold and ivory masterpiece, one of the wonders of the ancient world, the Olympian Zeus. Here the famous games were organized in honour of the god in the sanctuary of peace.[41] The games were in honour of Zeus the god who wore a crown of olive leaves. The Olympic victor received a crown, not of gold, but of wild olive! It is at least strange that the god, the mountain and the olive should be so closely associated. And the constant messenger of Zeus was Iris—the rainbow!

Noah probably deduced very little for certain from the failure of the raven to return but the evidence of the dove was obviously valuable. The flood was now down far enough for the olive trees to be uncovered and a week later the trees were so far clear of water that the dove had presumably settled among them. Yet it was still many days before Noah finally left the Ark and we must therefore conclude that the Ark itself was grounded somewhere well above the olive tree line and very much above the surrounding valleys. The Ark may likely enough have been resting on some level area at a height of perhaps 4000 to 8000 feet above the general countryside. Even if the Ark were grounded at only 2000 feet above the plain the water must have fallen (or the whole region risen) at a rate of nearly ten feet a day for it was 221 days from the time of grounding on Ararat to the final leaving of the Ark.[42]

But where, indeed, did the Ark rest? The Hebrew account specifies the mountains (plural) of Ararat suggesting that the name is used for a district and not for a particular peak. The Hebrew Ararat occurs again in II Kings 19. 37, Isaiah 37. 38 and Jeremiah 51. 27, but on the two former occasions it is rendered by the AV Armenia. The Revised Version retains 'Ararat'. The name seems to be identical with the Urartu of ancient inscriptions, a term applied to the land which the Greeks called Armenia[43] and a region frequently referred to in Assyrian records.[44] Some have said that the name Ararat means 'Holy Land'[45] but it is perhaps more probable that it means 'mountainous region', and accounts outside the Bible have fixed on many mountainous regions as the site of the Ark's grounding. The Gilgamesh Epic fixes on Mt. Nisir—a name usually supposed to apply to a mountain much further south than Ararat and near to the Lower Zab although some have thought that Nisir might be the mighty Elburz range itself.[46] Certain it is that all ancient accounts fasten upon some mountain—Parnassus, Olympus, Eryx, the Himalayas, or for the inhabitants of Mexico, or Peru or

Polynesia, some local mountain. But despite the claims of all these peaks, so obviously brought into the stories later, Ararat remains the only reasonable claimant to be the site of the grounding of the Ark.

Josephus, who twice maintains that some of the timber of the Ark was still extant in his day, locates the mountain in Armenia.[47] He says that the Armenians called the place Apobaterion—the Place of Descent or Disembarking. Nicolaus of Damascus reports that there is a 'great mountain in Armenia, over Minyas called Baris' on which the Ark came to rest.[48] Whiston quotes the Armenian historian, Moses Chorenensis, as saying that the place was known locally as Nachidsheuan—the place of descent—and there is still a place of that name to this day. Moses Chorenensis also speaks of a place called Seron—the place of dispersion— because from there the descendants of Noah began to disperse. Berossus, who asserts that the Armenians made bracelets and amulets from its wood, says that the Ark remained among the Kordyean Mountains.[49]

The name Ararat, which was originally applied to the whole land, has gradually become restricted to a huge volcanic mountain mass covering an area twenty-five miles long by twelve miles broad and lying between the great lakes Van, Sevang and Urmia. It lies also about midway between the Black Sea and the Caspian, two seas which are known to have been connected in the past, although the Caspian is now eighty-five feet below the level of the Black Sea and Lake Urmia, which is a salt lake,[50] is 4200 feet above sea level! This immense volcanic mass rises to two peaks both of which are difficult to climb and hence are known locally as Aghri-Dagh or Difficult Mountain. Buyuk Aghri-Dagh or Greater Ararat is about 17,000 feet while Kuçuk Aghri-Dagh is about 12,800 feet. The bases of these mountains are about seven miles apart but the two masses meet in a col at 8800 feet. The lower zones have a few birch trees and the middle reaches, from 5000 to 10,000 feet, have pastures. The upper reaches of Greater Ararat are bare and wildly impressive with great masses of lava, cinders and porphyry and finally snow with

glaciers towards the 14,000 feet level. The region is still known
to the Armenians as Massis or Varez Baris and to the Persians as
Koh-i-Nuh, the mountain of Noah. That the volcano is not
extinct but merely dormant was proved by the great earthquake
of July 1840 which was accompanied by red smoke and a smell
of sulphur. It made considerable changes in the aspect of the
mountain and destroyed the monastery of St. James near
Arghuri—the village which claimed to be the site of Noah's
vineyard. The region is said to abound with names and legends
of the Flood[51] but how far these are independent of the Hebrew
account it is now impossible to say. Mention has been made of
names like Cemainum (=eight), Tabriz or Ta Baris (the ship)
Nachsivan (the burial place of Noah) and Marand, which claims
to be the burial place of Noah's wife.

We must look briefly at the modern ascents, searches and
claims that have been made on and around Ararat.

For many years travellers who came near the mountain were
shown in the distance, sometimes through a telescope, an object
high up on the mountain side which the local folk claimed to be
the prow of the Ark. Investigation has shown this to be a spur of
rock.[52]

The mountain was first climbed by Dr. Parrot in September
1829. In 1840 a great earthquake, undoubtedly connected with
volcanic activity although not an actual eruption, destroyed the
village of Arghuri and the monastery of St. James and caused
new fissures on the north side of Ararat. A team of Turkish
workmen sent to consider defences against avalanches after the
disaster claimed to have found the prow of an ancient vessel
emerging from a glacier and experts are said to have followed up
the investigation and entered three compartments of the vessel.[53]
In 1893 the Archdeacon of Jerusalem, Dr. Nouri, is said to have
seen the prow and stern of a ship whose central portions were
buried in snow. He says that the wood was red, very thick and
joined by 12 inch nails.[54]

There are two war-time stories, neither of which rests on any
satisfactory evidence whatever. The first is from 1916. A

Russian airman named Roskovitsky, while flying in the region of Ararat claimed to have seen the remains of a huge vessel grounded in a blue lake. He reported this to his superior officer and word was sent to the Czar who is alleged to have sent an expedition of 150 men to investigate the phenomenon. These are said to have taken photos of the structure which was made of great timbers, with many rooms, some enclosed by huge wooden bars and others by wrought iron (!) All was coated with a wax-like substance. There had been a 20 foot door which was missing. The roof was curved and had a narrow cat-walk along the top. The account was, according to Roskovitsky, brought back to Russia but was entirely destroyed during the Bolshevik revolution (!!) Roskovitsky escaped to America where his account was published in various forms.

No evidence has ever been forthcoming that there is an atom of truth in this story or in a similar one told in the second world war when some Russians are reported to have found the remains of a huge vessel 3900 feet long (!)

The claims of Fernand Navarra are interesting.[55] He and his party in 1952 scaled Ararat and also investigated the blue lake Kop but without finding any trace of the Ark. On their journey, however, above the lake and at about 13,800 feet they observed, encased in ice and a matter of yards below the surface, what appeared to them to be the black form of a vessel with curving sides and of length about 450 feet. This they believed to be the Ark. They had no means whatever of excavating into solid ice and their report adds no more.

A curious aerial photograph was published in the Daily Telegraph for 13 September 1965. This reveals a very clear boat-like outline on a wild mountain slope said to be a part of the volcanic region of Ararat. The outline is pointed at each end and is said to be about 400 feet long. The sides or outlines are marked by what looks like ridges in lava. Geologists in England, judging apparently entirely from the photograph, have dismissed the phenomenon as merely a freak of volcanic action followed by weathering.

While rejecting some of the above accounts completely it is probably wisest to keep an open mind on the other pieces of evidence and hope that further exploration will finally settle one way or the other the problem of the existence of the Ark on Ararat.

When at last the long-awaited Divine command came, Noah opened the door of the Ark, and he and his family and all the living creatures that had been with them made their way out into a New World. Noah's first act was to build an altar and offer sacrifices of clean beasts and birds to God. This is the first mention in the Bible of an altar, although we may wonder whether Abel, who also offered an animal sacrifice, had made some simple construction that could have been so called. Certainly the conception of bringing sacrifices to God goes back to the days of Cain and Abel.

That Noah did indeed offer up sacrifices is maintained not only in the Biblical account but also by a number of other ancient records. In the account as given by Berossus and transmitted through Alexander Polyhistor we are told that Xisuthrus 'paid his adoration to the earth and having constructed an altar, offered sacrifices to the gods'. Ut-napishtim in the Gilgamesh Epic (X. 156 ff.) declares 'I offered a sacrifice, I poured out a libation on the top of the mountain; I set up seven and seven cult-vessels, upon their stands I heaped cane, cedar-wood and myrtle. The gods smelled the sweet savour, they crowded like flies around the sacrifices. At length, as the Great Goddess (Ishtar) arrived she lifted up the great jewels which Anu had made. Ye gods, as surely as this lapis upon my neck I shall not forget: I shall be mindful of those days and never forget them'.

This account is quite obviously a much later, very crude and twisted, polytheistic version of the facts which are set out so much more clearly and accurately in the Bible. It will be observed that not only have we the sacrifices but, as in Genesis, a 'sweet savour' and also the goddess Ishtar with her lapis necklace as the sign that she will remember. Here we have, distorted as usual with Babylonian legends, the rainbow and the covenant.

In the Greek account Deucalion built an altar and even con-
secrated a temple to Juno. Manu in the Indian story worshipped
God and offered sacrifices. So did the 'Noah' of the Polynesian
and Maori stories even if, as in the latter case, the offering was
only sea-weed!

That the idea of sacrifices and offerings was well known to
Noah seems evident from the story. Obviously, too, provision
had been made for it by the taking into the Ark of the sevens of
clean beasts and birds. It is further evident that the classification
of animals into clean and unclean was well known to Noah
although on what basis the classification was then made does not
appear.[56]

These early offerings are described as burnt offerings but the
actual Hebrew term means 'that which ascends' i.e. to God.
From the fact that in later ritual the entire creature (apart from
the skin) was consumed such offerings became known as 'whole
burnt offerings' from the LXX Holocaust. Thus in very simple
fashion did Noah try to express his attitude to God—to the God
who had delivered him from death—to the God who was holy
and had destroyed those unrepentant folk who neither listened
to the preaching nor attempted to enter the only means of
safety. And God responds in just as simple a fashion by de-
scribing Noah's attitude as a 'savour of satisfaction', and by
making the rainbow the beautiful symbol of a solemn covenant.

The rainbow has not entirely disappeared from the legendary
accounts of the Flood. The rainbow was Ishtar's lapis-lazuli
necklace. The rainbow goddess Iris[57] was the constant attendant
upon Zeus. She was the messenger between gods and men and
came from a mountain—Ida or Olympus. To the Basuto tribe
there were four rainbows after the Flood—one in each direction,
and the Hawaiian people speak of a god who came down the
rainbow to speak to Nu-u.[58] Even to our Norse ancestors Bifrost
was the Rainbow Bridge between gods and men—the bridge that
will continue down the years, to be destroyed at last at Ragnarok,
the great final struggle of the gods.

So the rainbow became the simple sign in the material world

I

of God's covenant—and a new age of the world began. Each succeeding age has had its outward and material sign: circumcision and the sabbath for the Old Covenant, and a loaf of bread, a cup of wine and the water of baptism for the New Covenant—that Covenant which is indeed the beginning, not merely of a new era but of a New Creation. And to the Christian there lies behind that Covenant a sacrifice not of birds and beasts on a wild mountain side called Ararat, but of the Son of God Himself on a mound called Calvary.

Some of the older commentators[59] believed that the rainbow appeared for the first time after the flood. Some, basing their ideas on Genesis 2. 5, 6, assert that in fact it had not rained until the Flood. This view has been defended in recent times by Morris and Whitcomb[60] but their extremely short paragraph on the subject is unfortunately devoid of any reasonable evidence in its favour. The interpretation of Genesis 2. 5, 6, is uncertain and it would seem to apply to the region around Eden (the 'earth' is probably the 'land') and to the times before, not after, Adam was responsible for the care of that zone. Alford[61] maintains that the text merely means that the water rose from the earth as mist and descended ('watered the face of the ground') as rain. So far as the rainbow is concerned the text does not demand that the rainbow had never appeared before the Flood. Rather does God take a familiar thing and make it the sign or symbol of a covenant.[62] Circumcision and the sabbath were known before the Exodus—even before Abram—but they *became* signs of God's covenant. Baptism and a ceremonial meal were known before Christ but they became the symbols of the New Covenant.

God has kept His promise. Seed time and harvest, cold and heat, summer and winter, day and night have not ceased. Whatever vast uprisings and sinkings of continents may have—indeed must have—taken place in earlier Pleistocene times there has been no great earth movement since the Flood. God has remembered His covenant.

Whether we can discern one little trace of something more behind these words I do not know. Perhaps there is the faintest suggestion that the upheaval which caused the Flood was so vast that for a short time it had altered or threatened the stability of the very seasons. There have been those who have surmised that the cause of the Flood was the shifting of the earth's axis. The poles migrated; what was once forest or grassland became tundra, and fertile regions became deserts.[63] Astronomers at present can find no adequate force to cause so great a movement in so short a time. While all agree that the poles have in the past slowly wandered no geologist is prepared to admit a wholesale sudden shift in the polar axis in the Pleistocene period. Yet the strange stories of the mammoths and the bone caves, and the curious characters of lakes and seas like the Caspian, and Aral[64] and Van, the peculiarities of lakes high up in the Andes, the vast smashed forests and buried animal remains of the Arctic Islands and numerous other phenomena of like kind scattered across the world make one pause. At present it is better to take the only reasonable course and confess that we just do not know. We leave the question open. The causes of the Flood, and indeed of all great earth movements, are still largely beyond our understanding, let alone calculation.[65] By admitting that we do not know, we leave the door wide open for further knowledge.

The Bible is always true to life. Noah, described in the record as a righteous man, set forward as an example of almost incredible faith, was nevertheless, like every other member of the human race, a sinner. In its wonderful honesty the Bible tells us of the weakness of the greatest saints, so that ultimately Jesus Christ alone stands out as the sinless One.

Noah became drunk[66] and was mocked by his younger son. The lack of respect, even of common decency,[67] shown by Ham has crept into many heathen legends of the gods, often grossly exaggerated and distorted, in tales that tell of some ancient god not merely mocking but mutilating his father. Such sordid stories we leave to heathenism. Noah was guilty, and the fact that his sin was put on record for all his descendants to read has surely been its own terrible punishment.

But as Noah recovered soberness so, as in a waking moment,

his eyes were opened and he saw, not only the events of the past
few minutes or hours, but he saw down the centuries of history.
He saw, stretching before him, the countless generations descended from that proud and disrespectful son, becoming servants
to the races descended from those who, practising greater self-
discipline, would build the sturdier and dominant races.

Noah, we are told, began to be a husbandman, and planted a
vineyard and drank wine. We may enquire whether, in fact, it is
reasonable to attribute these activites to one living so far back in
history and in so remote a region as Armenia. Here, once again,
as in every tiny detail of the story, the answer is emphatically,
yes. There is now little doubt about the time when settled agri-
cultural work began, or about the region in which it was developed. As the neolithic age progressed—the times following
the Flood—so settled agriculture steadily developed in the
regions around the Caspian Sea. Mrs. Sonia Cole in her book on
the Neolithic Revolution[68] speaks of the rise of agriculture in the
area from Palestine and Syria to the Zagros range between Iraq
and Iran. She speaks of the 'new way of life' which developed
along the foothills of the Zagros mountains and the plains of
Anatolia. Maps in her book show the beginnings of the use of
wild einkorn in Turkey and of two-row barley across Asia Minor
and North Persia. From this centre the wheat and grain areas
reached into Europe, Egypt and the Indus Valley. As we have
seen, in the latter places, alongside the development of metal
industries there were the great granaries of the Nile valley and
of Harappa. Prof. Coon in his *History of Man*[69] traces the origin
of agriculture to the same area—from Anatolia to Pakistan and
from Turkestan to Arabia.[70]

So far as the cultivation of the vine is concerned we find that
the modern plant is descended from a species which was indigenous to the region of the Caucasus. Alcoholic fermentation was
known in late Palaeolithic times and wine was definitely known
in Neolithic times. It was known in Pre-dynastic Egypt and also
in the Jamdat Nasr period before the First dynasty of Babylon.
Uru Kagina of Lagash (? 2400 B.C.) drank wine and Gudea

(? 2100 B.C.) built protected terraces for his vineyards.[71] There is an early record of 29,000 vines at Haran. We have, then, overwhelming evidence that Noah and his family and early descendants, occupying the area between the Mediterranean, the Black Sea, the Caspian Sea and the Indus Valley were the pioneers in agriculture and that Noah could easily have planted a vineyard and by fermentation have produced wine.

From that same area, so the Bible finally asserts, the new civilization started, and with the Divine blessing Noah's descendants, partly enumerated in the subsequent chapters, spread out across the face of the earth. It would require volumes to investigate all the evidence for this. One would have to study the spread of pottery,[72] of art, of building, of metallurgy, of agriculture, of writing and literature, of religious beliefs and political and social patterns as well as blood-groups and anatomical features. We have already seen that the history of agriculture and grain-cultivation confirms the Biblical account. That the earliest forms of writing are found in the regions between Crete and the Indus Valley, and particularly towards the centre of that area, is well known.

We may, in bringing this long section to its conclusion, follow just one recent line of discovery as illustrative of the others. Investigations of the origin of metallurgy have shown, as was long suspected, that in certain areas metal working goes back almost to the beginning of the Neolithic period.[73] Thus the Caucasus region and the areas around the Caspian were in their 'Copper Age' while lands not far away were still following a Neolithic way of life. In the latest great two-volume *History of Metals*[74] the author declares that not only do suitable copper ores and wood for smelting-furnaces occur in the Caucasus and around Lake Van and in the Elburz mountains but 'one of the most likely places for the origin of copper smelting is Armenia'.[75] From this centre the knowledge of metallurgy spread to Sumeria, to Persia and to the Indus Valley, to the Hittites and to Egypt and, more slowly, through South Russia to Europe.

Agriculture, metallurgy and writing were obviously three of

the greatest factors in the development of the new civilization
which emerged after the Flood. Agriculture and metallurgy
commenced in the Armenia–Caspian–North Persian area, and
writing originated somewhere between Asia Minor and the
Indus Valley. There is sufficient proof that the Biblical account
of the spread of a new race from a centre known as Armenia is
absolutely true.

Thus from the first statement about the Flood to the last in the
book of Genesis every verse that can be questioned, examined
and tried has stood the test. We have called on History, Archaeology, Geology, Radio-activity, Botany, Geography, Shipbuilding, Mythology and Metallurgy to produce their evidence.
Not one sentence of the Biblical account, carefully interpreted in
its context, can be shown to be incorrect or second-hand or even
to be unrealistic or unlikely. It is the recorded, reliable account
of an eye-witness. Our survey of the evidence is finished.

It is recorded of the great scientist, Michael Faraday, that he
was sitting one day before an open Bible with his head bowed
and with tears in his eyes. A friend, laying his hand on him,
asked him if he was unwell. 'No,' said Faraday, 'it is not that.
Why, oh why, will not people believe this Book?' This, the
strangest and saddest part of our study, we shall look at in the
next chapter.

NOTES

1. Genesis 6. 22.
2. The curious word 'selfsame' day in Genesis 7. 13 has never been ex-
   plained. It is so ancient that its derivation has been lost. The Hebrew
   'etsem' seems originally to have meant 'bone-day'. It is used in the Bible
   for the date of the covenant with Abraham, Genesis 17. 23, 26; for the
   date when Israel came out of Egypt, Exodus 12. 17, 41, 51; for the day of
   atonement, Leviticus 23.14; for the day of the death of Moses, Deuteronomy 32. 48; for the end of the manna, Joshua 5. 11 and for the day
   when Nebuchadnezzar approached Jerusalem, Ezekiel 24. 2. Some have
   suggested that it has a particular calendar reference, e.g. to some day of the
   week, like Sunday or Friday, or to some anniversary.
3. I. P. Cory, *Ancient Fragments*, p. 32.
4. See J. Skinner, *Genesis*, p. 135. D. Kidner, *Genesis*, p. 83, leans to the
   view that the 'life-spans are intended literally'.
5. I. P. Cory, *Ancient Fragments*, p. 89.
6. See G. C. Vaillant, *The Azteks of Mexico*, pp. 68, 69. Quetzalcoatl or
   Huemac (pronounced Weymac) is described as 'a marvellous personage

who brought civilization and ethics. He compiled a book of history and prophecy and died at the age of 300'. In the Bible Enoch is described as righteous, prophesying the destruction of the ungodly, and living 365 years.

7. Josephus, *Antiquities* I. 3. 9.
8. S. Langdon, *The Venus Tablets of Ammizaduga.*
9. A. Marshack, *Lunar Notation on Upper Palaeolithic Remains, 'Science'*, Vol. 146. 6 November, 1964, p. 743.
10. Exodus 12. 2. The English equivalents of the dates of Noah's calendar given in the older edition of Scofield Bible are completely in error being all six months out due to failure to observe the change at the Exodus. They are omitted in the new edition of the Scofield Bible.
11. Josephus, *Antiquities* 1. 3. 3., stresses that it was the Hebrew month Marcheswan. He adds that it was the Macedonian month Dius. This, too, is very interesting for the Macedonian month Dios was the first month of the Macedonian year and it looks as if this calendar, like others to which we shall refer, started in November from the anniversary of the Flood. Still more interesting is the name, for Dios is but another form of Zeus and while it is not possible to say for certain that Zeus is a distorted recollection of Noah, the resemblance to the name Zius-udra is at least curious. See further evidence, note 39.
12. A. Hislop, *The Two Babylons*, pp. 136, 137.
13. Plutarch, *On Isis and Osiris*, Athyr is a variant of Hathor the goddess who was guardian of the tombs of the dead.
14. S. Langdon, *Babylonian Menologies and the Semitic Calendar*, p. 36. In Babylon, however, the ceremonies were in the previous month, Teshrit.
15. Ibid., p. 129.
16. J. Frazer, *Golden Bough*, 1 volume edition, p. 633.
17. Samhain is the Celtic New Year festival held at the beginning of November. (E. Sykes, *Dictionary of Non-Classical Mythology*, s.v.).
18. G. S. Faber, quoting Davies' *Mythology of the British Druids*, p. 517 says 'Bardic songs are yet extant in which is celebrated the return of the mythological Arthur with his seven companions from their voyage over a boundless ocean, beneath the waves of which all the rest of mankind had been overwhelmed'.
19. Berossus, from Abydenus. I. P. Cory, *Ancient Fragments*, p. 34.
20. J. B. Pritchard, *The Ancient Near East*, pp. 69, 70. Prof. S. N. Kramer, writing in THE TIMES (14 November, 1964) refers to a newly translated Sumerian tablet which tells of a raven being seized by Inanna the wife of Dumuzi the shepherd-god whose sheepfolds were destroyed by the Flood.
21. Plutarch, *De Sol. Animal*, p. 968 quoted from Faber, *Horae Mosaicae*.
22. See p. 55. It must also be remembered that the introduction of two new months, July and August, shifted the old November to January.
23. G. S. Faber, *Horae Mosaicae*, p. 124.
24. A. P. Stanley, *Sinai and Palestine*, p. 257, speaks of the sacred doves kept at Ascalon for Derceto in the time of Eusebius. Xenophon, *Anabasis* I. 4., says that the Syrians protected the dove. Doves are sacred among Mohammedans and Hindus.
25. G. S. Faber, *Horae Mosaicae*, p. 126.
26. Judges 7. 25. The two princes of Midian were *OREB*, Raven and *ZEEB*, Wolf.
27. Even today in Ireland the raven is regarded as the bird of knowledge.
28. The Hebrew *OREB* means raven, crow or any bird of that type.
29. I Kings 17. 4–6.
30. M. Kalisch understands the Hebrew to mean that the raven came back to the Ark but Alford, *Commentary on Genesis*, p. 37, thinks this improbable and the raven lived on the carcasses of animals that were scattered about.

31. *Chambers Encyclopaedia*, Art. *Dove*. G. S. Faber states that the Argonauts also sent out doves from the Argo, *Horae Mosaicae*, p. 124.
32. The French army used them at the siege of Paris and at the battle of the Somme. See also W. M. Levi, *The Pigeon*, Ch. 1. for details of many amazing flights made by pigeons in World Wars I and II. Through mist and storm and shrapnel literally hundreds of pigeons got through with their messages saving the lives of thousands of wrecked or marooned airmen and of troops cut off by enemy forces. Several stories tell of pigeons getting their messages through despite serious injury, one having lost a leg and another an eye. The pigeon 'William of Orange' released a Arnhem in September 1944 brought a message safely to its loft, 260 miles in 4½ hours. Pigeons are raced up to 600 miles.
33. W. Thomson, *The Land and the Book*, p. 51. C. Singer, *History of Technology*, Vol. 1. p. 359. See also above p. 113, for further connections with Zeus. The dove and the olive are also shown on the coins of Apamea from Phrygia. See p. 45.
34. See *Oxford Classical Dictionary* and *Encyclopaedia Britannica*, Article Olive, and C. Singer, *History of Technology*, Vol. I. p. 359.
35. W. Thomson, *The Land and the Book*, p. 51.
36. Quoted from H. Alford, *Commentary on Genesis*.
37. *Oxford Classical Dictionary*, p. 966. 'Zeus is the only Greek god whose Indo-European origin can be proved with certainty'. Cf. German Ziu.
38. Liddell and Scott, *Lex.*, suggest Sanskrit *DYAUI* became Jove. DY could easily be changed to Z or J and of course U =V in Latin.
39. Zeus is sometimes spelt *DEUS* (Liddell and Scott) and he is also *ZEN* (rain). The epithet Father of gods and men comes from Homer, but if Zeus is also a reflection of the Deluge-age patriarchs and if the gods are mainly the rebels of Flood-Babel times, then, of course, Zeus was father of gods and men. As *DEUS PATER* he became *JUPITER* to the Romans. See also *Encyclopaedia Britannica*, Art. Sanskrit Language.
40. *Encyclopaedia Britannica*, Art. Olympus. See also references in Liddell and Scott. *The Oxford Classical Dictionary*, p. 966, says that Olympus is a pre-Greek word meaning 'mountain'.
41. No soldiers were allowed in Olympia. The place was a religious sanctuary long before classical times. The olive leaves given to the Olympic victor were cut from a special tree growing in the enclosure of the Temple of Zeus. In Athens there was, according to Herodotus, Bk. VIII ch. 55, in the Temple of Erechtheus a sacred olive tree, planted by Athene and a well of salt water made by Poseidon (Neptune).
42. See E. F. Kevan, *New Bible Commentary*, (I.V.F.), pp. 84, 85.
43. R. Graves, *The Greek Myths*, Sect. 154. 12 says Armenia means 'High land of Minni'. Minni is probably the Minyas mentioned by Josephus, *Antiquities* 1. 1. 6 in connection with the Flood. A brief summary of Armenian history is given in Young's *Concordance* under ARMENIA. See also *Encyclopaedia Britannica*.
44. From at least the times of Shalmaneser I, (1274–1245 B.C.), when it is referred to as Uratri.
45. See *Young's Concordance*, and *The Proper Names of the Old Testament*, (Anon), published by Williams and Norgate.
46. J. Skinner, *Genesis*, p. 166, quoting Tiele and Kosters. The Elburz range south of the Caspian, reaches its greatest height, 18,800 feet in Mt. Damavand, (higher than Ararat) and this range was sacred to the Iranians.
47. Josephus, *Antiquities* I. 3. 5, and XX, 2. 2. Theophilus of Antioch (second century A.D.) *Ad Autolycus*, Bk. 3. and Chrysostom both assert the same.
48. See above p. 44.
49. I. P. Cory, *Ancient Fragments*, p. 29 and footnote. Epiphanius speaks of the 'Gordyean Mountains', probably both being intended for Kurdistan. Epiphanius calls the mountain Lubar =descending place. Faber, *Horae Mosaicae*, p. 119. *The Book of the Cave of Treasures* (sixth century A.D.)

says that the Ark rested on the mountains of Kardu. This is a very ancient name for Armenia.

50. Lake Van is also salt, and contains some carbonate and sulphate as well. The whole of Armenia was completely submerged in earlier geological times. Lynch says that Miocene salt deposits extend right across Armenia though they have not produced the desolation which attends the great salt deserts of the Persian plateau. These are said to extend over a distance of 500 miles across land that is now 2000 or more feet above sea level. Lynch (Vol. II. p. 50) says 'We must not forget that at a period relatively recent in geological time this Lake Van was but a part of an extensive inland sea', and again (p. 50) he quotes the local tradition that Lake Van 'covers a plain that once had gardens and villages'.

51. By the side of Lake Van is the gigantic crater of the extinct Quaternary volcano Nimrod (Nimrut Dagh). This crater which Lynch gives as 14 miles in circumference is one of the largest in the world. It is now partly filled with a fresh water lake. Sulphurous bubbles rise at times to the surface. On the north side of Lake Van is another huge volcano Suphan Dagh where local tradition (probably quite imaginary) says that the Ark actually touched before grounding on Ararat. There are enormous masses of lava throughout the whole region. Nimrut Dagh is said to have erupted as recently as A.D. 1441.

52. Fernand Navarra, *The Forbidden Mountain*, p. 156.

53. In 1850 Col. Khoelzko with a party of sixty climbed the mountain for a trigonometrical survey but they saw nothing of the Ark.

54. Fernand Navarra, Ibid., pp. 24, 30.

55. Fernand Navarra, Ibid. 1956.

56. The fact that certain animal meat was forbidden as unclean in many ancient races shows that this classification goes back far beyond the time of Moses.

57. The Greek word in Revelation 4. 3 and 10. 1 for 'rainbow' is still 'iris'. In Genesis the ordinary word for bow is used. Bows and arrows are now known to have been used by Palaeolithic man. The bow would be quite familiar to Noah and his family.

58. The rainbow as a token of safety from floods is said to occur in both European and Asiatic folk-lore. Fohi, the first Emperor of China, was said to have been conceived when his mother was encompassed by a rainbow. He lived at the time of a deluge and at what was called 'The division of Time'. G. S. Faber, *Horae Mosaicae*, p. 139.

59. So Keil and F. Delitzsch but M. Kalisch takes the opposite view.

60. *The Genesis Flood*, p. 241. D. W. Patten also contends for a much higher water-vapour content of the air before the Flood. See *The Biblical Flood and the Ice Epoch*, p. 200.

61. *Commentary on Genesis*, p. 11.

62. The text may be correctly translated 'I appoint my bow' i.e. the rainbow which had existed long before was now 'appointed' to its new significance as a sign of God's Covenant.

63. There seems to have been a very long-term wandering of the actual poles as well as short-term movements and migrations of the magnetic pole. These can presumably only be due to slip of the earth's crust relative to the axis of rotation. See W. Bascom, *A Hole in the bottom of the Sea*, p. 170. I. Velikovsky, *Earth in Upheaval*, pp. 44, 46 quotes cases of magnolia and figs in North Greenland, giant sequoias around the Bering Strait evidences of conifers within 5° of the South Pole and of coral in the Arctic.

64. The Caspian Sea is only one-third as salt as other oceans and the Aral Sea is almost fresh. Although the Caspian Sea is completely land-locked it contains seals related to the Arctic seal. Professor Austin Miller, *Climatology*, p. 300 attributes the filling of the present Caspian and Aral seas to the times of the Flandrian Transgression.

65. Beno Gutenberg, *The Internal Constitution of the Earth*, (2nd. edition, 1951), p. 74 gives a summary of thirteen of the forces or changes which may be operating on the surface of the earth.
66. There is no doubt a certain connection between Noah's drunkenness and the legends of Bacchus. Dionysus, also known to both Greeks and Romans as Bacchus, was originally the Phrygian god Diounsis. Diodorus Siculus, Bk. 3. Ch. 4 says that several gods have now become merged into one legend. Some say Bacchus, the inventor of wine, was the son of Zeus and Ceres (? agriculture), others, the son of Iris (the rainbow). He is also called Sabazius and Diodorus says was then depicted with horns because he was the first to yoke oxen to the plough for agriculture. He is called 'twice born', probably as starting a new life after the Flood. Diodorus says Dionysus was the same as Osiris and R. Graves, *Greek Myths*, Vol. I. Section 27. 6 says Dionysus was identical with Deucalion or Noah. Herodotus, Bk. II, 42 identifies Bacchus with Osiris.
67. When some grasping and jealous bishops came to Constantine the Great with stories of the alleged immoral acts of their rivals, Constantine is said to have rebuked them and to have declared that if he found a bishop in such a sad case he would have covered him with his own cloak rather than blazen his sin to the world.
68. S. Cole, *The Neolithic Revolution*, (British Museum, 1963). See. Ch. III 'Origins of Plant Cultivation', and also the chart on page vi showing how copper, bronze and neolithic civilizations could overlap.
69. C. S. Coon, *The History of Man*, pp. 124–128. The earliest traces of the domestication of sheep are found in the Elburz region, and of the domestic pig in caves around the Caspian Sea. *Op. cit.* p. 130. 'The most likely place in which to look for the beginnings of tillage and animal husbandry is the narrow belt of land lying between the Elburz mountains and the southern shore of the Caspian Sea. *Op. cit.* p. 139.
70. The earliest traces of food production in Mesopotamia come from Karim Shahir which lies east of the route down from Lake Van to Jarmo. Radio-carbon dates for the development of agriculture at Jarmo give 5000 B.C. or later. See H. W. F. Saggs, *The Greatness that was Babylon*, p. 7.
71. The vine is still widely cultivated in Armenia.
72. See, for example, the evidence from the 'Kerak' type of pottery, that the Hittites came from a Caucasian stock, in Sir Leonard Woolley's, *A Forgotten Kingdom*, pp. 31–35. One branch of Noah's descendants moved down into Persia and then divided, some going to the Indus Valley, the others being the Sumerians who came into Mesopotamia. See H. W. F. Saggs, *The Greatness that was Babylon*, p. 32.
73. 'Copper was known to the Egyptians in the early Predynastic Period, so that there is really but slight trace of a true Neolithic age in Egypt.' Introduction, *Guide to the Egyptian collections*, (British Museum, 1930), p. 147. It is now known that pre-dynastic furnaces would attain 1200 °C. and crude copper melts at about 1060 °C. The ore malachite can be reduced to give copper at about 800 °C.
74. L. Aitchison, *A History of Metals*, (London, 1960).
75. J. R. Partington, *Origins and Development of Applied Chemistry*, p. 226 says, 'It has been suggested that much of the metal work attributed to Assyria was actually made in Van. There are remains of very old copper mines in Armenia and the earliest copper of Egypt and Mesopotamia may have come from this region'.

CHAPTER 8

SOME IMPLICATIONS OF THE FLOOD

IT seems true that in this universe many changes proceed uniformly and slowly until some critical point beyond which they proceed with extreme and sometimes disastrous rapidity. Some of these are so common as to pass almost unnoticed. From early childhood we have watched a stick bend steadily—and then suddenly snap. We have watched a piece of elastic or a rubber balloon undergoing a uniform steady change—then a sudden burst. Sometimes it matters terribly. A great steel girder bends slightly under a strain—then a little more strain is thrown on it, and a little more—and suddenly it breaks and a vast structure is ruined. A steel hawser, by which a valiant little tug is trying to save a ship, is strained—it stretches almost imperceptibly—more and more—then snaps. The steam pressure in some boiler whose escape pipe is blocked rises steadily; there is no outward signal; it rises a little more and the engineering shop is wrecked by flying metal. Great dark clouds drift across the sky. Vast electric charges build up. For a short time there is an unseen leakage—then the dazzling flash of lightning.

The inhabitants of Pompeii and Herculaneum went about their daily work and enjoyed their nightly pleasures. Once, very suddenly, in A.D. 63 the earth suddenly shook beneath them and ruined many of their temples and finer buildings. But Pompeii and Herculaneum were soon being rebuilt. One by one the buildings were being restored. There was no visible change in the great mountain which overlooked their cities. All would be well. Then, with dramatic suddenness, on 24 August A.D. 79 Vesuvius, which had been rumbling for days, underwent a most violent eruption pouring out poisonous fumes, ashes, dust, stones and lava. Those cities whose immoralities were painted on their very walls, those places whose wickedness was such that some ancient inhabitant had inscribed the word Sodom on a wall —were suddenly enveloped in a destruction almost, but not quite, unparalleled in history. Not quite, for had not the kings of Sodom and Gomorrah lived equally in a fool's paradise? What change could they discern around them? True there were masses of oily bitumen in the nearby 'slime' pits and sometimes floating on the Dead Sea. True there was sometimes a sulphurous smell around the lake. And what importance could they attach to a mere foreigner like Lot who told them their deeds were evil? But the long slow changes in the oil-bearing rocks and bitumen pits around them one day passed a critical point. Lot fled. The region exploded. The great rift valley of the Dead Sea was shaken and torn. Masses of blazing pitch and sulphur and molten salt were flung into the air destroying for ever the cities of the plain. The dense clouds of black smoke were visible to Abraham many miles away.

The story is the same for Lisbon suddenly rocked by a terrible earthquake on 1 November 1755 with a series of shocks which killed 60,000 people in a few minutes; shocks which were felt over a million square miles. So, too, with Krakatoa 26–28 August 1883, the greatest of all modern eruptions, growling steadily for a number of days before throwing up steam and ashes and finally bursting and flinging a mountain—millions of tons into the sky, darkening land a hundred miles away, throwing the sea into such waves that 36,000 people on Java and Sumatra were drowned and a Dutch warship was hurled two miles inland!

We might continue indefinitely: San Francisco[1], Alaska, Messina, Quetta, Sagami Bay, Agadir, Skoplje—the story repeats itself with monotonous and terrible emphasis. Great changes come suddenly.

And it seems that even great stars 'burn' steadily for years until they reach some critical limit of size or temperature—and then explode to give new stars—the so-called Novae.

But men do not want to listen to this. Here is a strange

psychological or religious problem. The changes on the earth, they say, are relatively very small. The changes on the stars are too far away. They assure us that nothing untoward will happen for millions of years. All things really continue as they are. We have nothing to fear. Men will not learn the lesson. Great changes come suddenly.

Are we really sure that great continental movements have ceased for all time? God has kept His promise that the world should not be subjected to another great Flood. But the New Testament writers speak of a greater destruction to come—not by water but by fire! They insist that this final catastrophe will come suddenly—come as a thief in the night—come when men do not expect it. It will come when men are saying, 'Peace and Security'.

Let us turn, then, to the New Testament and weigh carefully once again the words of the apostles and of Christ Himself. Paul writes to the Thessalonians in his first epistle (ch.5. 1–3 AV and RV): 'But concerning the times and the seasons, brethren, ye have no need that I write to you. For you know perfectly that the day of the Lord so comes as a thief in the night. For when they shall say, Peace and safety, then sudden destruction comes upon them', and in his second epistle (ch. 1. 6–10): 'Seeing it is a righteous thing with God to recompense affliction to them that afflict you, and to you that are afflicted rest with us when the Lord Jesus shall be revealed from heaven with the angels of His power in flaming fire rendering vengeance to them that know not God and that obey not the gospel'. In the next chapter he refers again to those who will neither believe nor heed the warnings, on whom falls the great delusion or lie (II Thess. 2. 11).

The writer to the Hebrews, quoting partly from the Psalms, sees the same astronomical upheaval. 'Thou, Lord, in the beginning hast laid the foundation of the earth, and the heavens are the works of thy hands: They shall perish; but thou remainest; and they shall all wax old as doth a garment; and as a vesture shalt Thou fold them up, and as a garment they shall be changed' (Heb. 1. 10–12 AV and RV).

Peter, too, is equally certain of the coming of a sudden destruction upon a generation deluded into a sense of security (II Peter 3. 3, 4, 7–10 AV and RV). 'There shall come in the last days scoffers, walking after their own lusts, and saying, Where is the promise of His coming? For since the fathers fell asleep, all things continue as they were from the beginning of creation . . . But the heavens and the earth which are now, are kept in store, reserved unto fire against the day of judgment and destruction of ungodly men.' 'But, beloved, forget not this one thing, that one day is with the Lord as a thousand years, and a thousand years as one day . . . But the day of the Lord will come as a thief, in the which the heavens shall pass away with a great noise, and the elements shall melt with fervent heat, the earth also and the works that are therein shall be burned up'.

John in the Revelation frequently sees this same final judgment, recorded under several different symbols. He, too, sees the sweeping away by fire of the old order and looks for a new and purified world.

We turn last of all to the most important of all, the words of Christ Himself; the words which He claimed that He spoke, not from Himself alone, but from God the Father—the God in whose hand and ultimate control all the future lies. His words are simple and direct. 'As it was in the days of Noah even so shall it be also in the days of the Son of Man. They ate, they drank, they married, they were given in marriage, until the day that Noah entered into the Ark, and the flood came, and destroyed them all' (Luke 17. 26, 27 AV and RV). Matthew (ch. 24. 36–42 AV and RV) gives our Lord's solemn warning in even greater detail: 'But of that day and hour knoweth no man, no, not the angels of heaven, but my Father only. But as were the days of Noah, so shall be the coming of the Son of Man. For as in the days that were before the Flood they were eating and drinking, marrying and giving in marriage, until the day that Noah entered into the ark, and they knew not until the Flood came, and took them all away; so shall also the coming of the Son of Man be. Then shall two men be in the field; the one shall be taken, and the other left. Two women shall be grinding at the mill; the one shall be taken and the other left. Watch therefore: for ye know not what hour your Lord cometh'. And finally, having reminded His hearers that if the householder had known at what hour the thief was coming he would have been well prepared for him, Jesus repeats the tremendous warning and prophecy: 'Therefore be ye also ready: for in such an hour as ye think not THE SON OF MAN COMETH'.

We are left with an inescapable conclusion. The Flood was not only a real historical event; it was an event of immense theological significance.

The Flood is a real historical event. It is as certain as any of the other great facts of early history. It is proved by the careful records of the Hebrews, substantiated by the records of the Sumerians, Babylonians, Assyrians, Greeks and in lesser degrees by the ancient literature or records of many other lands. It is supported by the most careful researches into geology, ethnology, archaeology, chronology, and climatology and by following various lesser but intriguing lines of study. The accumulated evidence is far greater than that for many of the accepted facts of ancient history.

But we must fairly face the fact that men do not want to believe it or the warnings which follow from it. Hence their acceptance of the great delusion. 'All things continue as they were. Any catastrophes in the past have been relatively small, any changes very slow in coming. We need not worry. Peace and safety are before us for millions of years to come. No vast, sudden world-wide catastrophe awaits us. All is well!' And so the geological evidence has been distorted and most of the real evidence shelved, forgotten or quietly passed over. The Biblical evidence has been systematically undermined by the constantly repeated assertion that the account is copied from the Sumerian and that it was not finally put into writing until more than 700 years after Moses. Much archaeological evidence has been obscured by taking the so-called astronomical or higher datings for palaeolithic remains. Thus, while many among ordinary folk still believe in the Flood, these things are 'hid from the wise and prudent', so that few writers on ancient history or on the book of Genesis are prepared to accept what has been maintained in this book, that the Genesis account is a completely reliable, first-hand account of a vast geological upheaval.

The evidence is sufficient for all who are willing to believe. The writer is convinced that no evidence will ever satisfy those who do not want to believe.

But the Flood is not only an event of history. It is the age-long warning of God to the world. It is not only something that did happen . . . it is the pattern of something that will happen. In the words of Christ Himself (Matt. 24. 37 RV)

> As were the days of Noah
> So shall be the coming of the Son of man.

NOTE

1. San Francisco was destroyed by two shocks the greater of which lasted 25 seconds. The Quetta earthquake of 31 May 1935 took place at 3.3 a.m. Thirty seconds later 30,000 people were dead or injured.

APPENDIX 1

NOAH'S 'WINDOW' AND THE 'PHILOSOPHER'S STONE'

THE subsequent history of the word *TSOHAR* for Noah's window is extremely curious and illustrates the point that some of the words used in the Flood story are so ancient that their true meanings were misunderstood even in very early times. From the fact that the account speaks of only one *TSOHAR* there grew up a Jewish legend that Noah was commanded to hang up a wonderful stone or gem[1] which would give light (*TSOHAR*) to all in the Ark.[2] This priceless gem was the Philosopher's Stone. In Greek legend Deucalion had the Philosopher's Stone in a bag but he lost it. The ancient world was constantly searching for this missing stone which was confused with the Philosopher's Egg, a kind of prime element, and also with the transmutation of the properties of base metals until they became gold. To the Arabic 'alchemists' this became also the elixir of life—that which would convey endless life. The stone lingered on in the Jewish writings like the Kabbalah. The Zohar—a book of Light—tells of the transmutation of metals. It is passing strange that the Persian name given to the most priceless diamond possessed by their country was *KOH-I-NOR*, 'mountain of Light',[3] especially as Ararat to them is *KOH-I-NUR* 'mountain of Noah'. But the connections of alchemy with the Flood emerge in other strange and devious ways. Clement of Alexandria and Tertullian, drawing on earlier Jewish writers, allege that ideas of alchemy, metallurgy and astronomy were brought to mankind by the fallen angels of Genesis 6. And legend has always attributed the word *CHEMIA* to *KHEM*, the name for Egypt the

land of *KHAM* (Biblical *HAM*), and the knowledge of this 'art'
to Hermes, the Egyptian *THOTH*. Jewish tradition alleges that
Hermes wrote the formula for making gold upon an emerald
tablet and this tablet came into the possession of Sarah, wife of
Abraham. Thus the secrets were passed down to the alchemists
and to the writers of the Jewish Kabbalah.

Such then is the wonderful web—without a single real thread
of support—which has been woven around Noah's *TSOHAR*.

NOTES

1. R. Graves, *Hebrew Myths*, p. 113 says it was a pearl hanging from the
   roof of the Ark, or possibly a book bound in sapphires containing knowledge of astronomy and medicine. Xisuthros had, according to Berossus,
   a book of wisdom, but this he buried at Sippur before the flood. See
   p. 40 above.
2. There may be a parallel thought in Revelation 21. 11 where it speaks of
   the Holy Jerusalem as 'having the glory of God: and her light was like
   unto a stone most precious, even like a jasper stone, clear as crystal'. The
   Kabbalah has drawn on some such metaphors.
3. See S. Tolansky, *The History and Use of Diamond*, (1962), p. 99

Appendix 2

TIME CHART

LONG CHRONOLOGY B.C.		SHORT CHRONOLOGY B.C.	
	Early Bronze		
3,000	Chalcolithic	2,500	
3,500	Neolithic	2,700	Local Floods
6,000	Mesolithic	3,000	
	Climatic Break		Noah's Flood
25,000	Upper Palaeolithic		
	Magdalenian	4,000	
			Upheavals after
	Solutrian		end of Ice Age
		6,000	
70,000	Aurignacian	8,000 +	
120,000	Middle Palaeolithic	+ +	
200,000	Lower Palaeolithic		
to			
1,000,000			

BIBLIOGRAPHY

AITCHISON, L.	*A History of Metals* London, 1960.
ALFORD, H.	*The Book of Genesis* London, 1872
ANATI, E.	*Palestine before the Hebrews* 1962
ARMSTRONG, E. A.	*The Folk-lore of Birds* London, 1958
BAILEY, E. B. and WEIR, J.	*Introduction to Geology* London, 1939.
BELLAMY, H. S.	*Moons, Myths and Man* London, 1949.
BIRCH, C.	*Chinese Myths and Fantasies* Oxford, 1961.
BROWN, F., DRIVER, S. R. and BRIGGS, C. A.	*A Hebrew and English Lexicon* Oxford, 1955.
BUDGE, E. A. WALLIS	*The Babylonian Story of the Deluge* London, 1920.
BURKITT, M. C.	*The Old Stone Age* London, 1963.
CARRIER, E. H.	*The Thirsty Earth* London, 1928.
CARRINGTON, R.	*Elephants* London, 1958.
CHARLESWORTH, J. K.	*The Quaternary Era* London, 1957.
CLARK, R. E. D.	*The Christian Stake in Science* Exeter, 1967.
CLINTON, H. F.	*Fasti Hellenici* Oxford, 1834.
COLE, SONIA	*The Neolithic Revolution* London, 1963.
COON, C. S.	*The History of Man* London, 1955.
CORY, I. P.	*Ancient Fragments* London, 1832.
DAVIDSON, F., STIBBS, A. M. and KEVAN, E. F.	*The New Bible Commentary* London, 1953.
DAVIDSON, H. R. ELLIS	*Gods and Myths of Northern Europe* London, 1964.
DIGBY, B.	*The Mammoth and Mammoth-Hunting in North-East Siberia* London, 1926.
DOUGLAS, J. D.	*The New Bible Dictionary* London, 1962.
DRIVER, S. R.	*The Book of Genesis* London, 1904.
Encyclopedia of Classical Mythology Englewood Cliffs, N. J. 1965.	
EHRICH, R. W.	*Chronologies in Old World Archaeology* Chicago, 1965.
EISSFELDT, OTTO	*The Old Testament. An Introduction*, Oxford, 1965.

FABER, G. S.   *Horae Mosaicae* London, 1818.
FRAZER, J. G.   *Folk-Lore in the Old Testament* London, 1923.
FRAZER, J. G.   *The Golden Bough* London, 1954.

GEIKIE, A.   *Textbook of Geology* London, 1882.
GRAVES, R.   *The Greek Myths* London, 1955.
GREEN, M.   *II Peter and Jude* I.V.F. Commentary London, 1968.
GUNTHER, J.   *Meet Central Africa* London, 1960.
GURNEY, O. R.   *The Hittites* London, 1954.
GUTENBERG, B.   *The Internal Constitution of the Earth* New York, 1951.

HASTINGS, J.   *Dictionary of the Bible* London, 1909 and 1963.
HAWKES, C. and J.   *Prehistoric Britain* London, 1943.
HISLOP, A.   *The Two Babylons* London, 1871.
HOLE, F. and HEIZER, *An Introduction to Prehistoric Archaeology* New
  R. F.   York, 1965.
HOOKE, S. H.   *Genesis* Peakes Commentary on the Bible 1962
HORNE, T. H.   *Introduction to the Scriptures* London, 1869

JESSUP, R.   *The Story of Archaeology in Britain* London, 1964.
JOLY, J.   *The Surface History of the Earth* Oxford, 1925.

KIDNER, D.   *Genesis* Tyndale Commentary London, 1967.
KING, L. C.   *The Morphology of the Earth* London, 1962.
KITCHEN, K. A.   *Ancient Orient and Old Testament* London, 1966.
KRAMER, S. N.   *History begins at Sumer* London, 1958.

LANDSTROM, B.   *The Ship* London, 1961.
LANGDON, S.   *Babylonian Menologies and Semitic Calendars* London, 1934.
LAROUSSE   *Encyclopedia of Mythology* London, 1962.
LEVI, W. M.   *The Pigeon* Sumter, S.C. U.S.A. 1963.
LIDDELL, H. G. and   *A Greek-English Lexicon* Oxford, 1940.
  SCOTT, R.
LUCAS, A.   *Ancient Egyptian Materials and Industries* London, 1948.
LYNCH, H. F. B.   *Armenia, Travels and Studies* London, 1901.

MCBURNEY, C. B. M.   *The Stone Age of Northern Africa* London, 1960.
MACQUEEN, J. G.   *Babylon* London, 1964.
MALLOWAN, M. E. L.   *Iraq* Vol. 26. Part 2. p. 62 1964.
MARTIN, W. J.   *Stylistic Criteria and the Analysis of the Pentateuch* London, 1955.
MILLARD, A. R.   *A New Babylonian 'Genesis' Story*, Tyndale Bulletin 18 (1967).
MILLER, A. AUSTIN   *Climatology* London, 1961.
MONKHOUSE, F. J.   *The Principles of Physical Geography* London, 1962.

Morris, H. M. and   *The Genesis Flood*   Philadelphia, 1962.
  Whitcomb, J. C.

Navarra, F.   *The Forbidden Mountain*   London, 1956.
Nelson, B. C.   *A History of the Flood Theory of Geology*   Min-
                             neapolis 1931.

Oakley, K. P.   *Frameworks for dating Fossil Man*   London, 1964.
O'Connell, P.   *Science of today and the problems of Genesis*   Min-
                             nesota, 1959.

Parrot, A.   *The Flood and Noah's Ark*   London, 1953.
Patten, D. W.   *The Biblical Flood and the Ice Epoch*   Seattle,
                             1966.
Peake, H.   *The Flood*   London, 1930.
Petrie, W. M. Flinders   *A History of Egypt*   London, 1903.
Piggott, S.   *Prehistoric India to 1,000 B.C.*   London, 1950.
Piggott, S.   *Approach to Archaeology*   London, 1959.
Plato   *Timaeus*   Translated by H. D. P. Lee   London,
                             1965.
Pratt, J. H.   *Scripture and Science not at Variance*   London,
                             1871.
Prestwich, J.   *On Certain Phenomena belonging to the close of the
                             last Geological Period*   London, 1895.
Pritchard, J. B.   *The Ancient Near East*   Princeton, 1958.

Raikes, R. L.   *Iraq*   Vol. 28   1966.
Ramm, B.   *The Christian View of Science and Scripture*
                             London, 1955.
Rehwinkel, A. M.   *The Flood in the Light of the Bible, Geology and
                             Archaeology*   Saint Louis, 1951.
Robinson, H. S. and   *Encyclopedia of Myths and Legends of all Nations*
  Wilson, K.   London, 1962.
Rogers, R. W.   *Cuneiform Parallels to the Old Testament*   New
                             York, 1926.
Rose, H. J.   *Handbook of Greek Mythology*   London, 1958.
Roux, G.   *Ancient Iraq*   London, 1964.

Saggs, H. W. F.   *The Greatness that was Babylon*   London,
                             1962.
Sanderson, I. T.   *The Dynasty of Abu . . . a History of the Elephants*
                             London, 1963.
Short, A. Rendle   *Modern Discovery and the Bible*   London, 1949.
Skinner, J.   *Genesis*   Edinburgh, 1930.
Smith, W. (Editor)   *Dictionary of the Bible*   London, 1863.
Smith, W. (Editor)   *Dictionary of Greek and Roman Biography and
                             Mythology*   London, 1844.
Sollberger, E.   *The Babylonian Legend of the Flood*   London,
                             1962.
Stamp, L. D.   *Man and the Land*   London, 1955.
Steers, J. A.   *The Coastline of England and Wales*   Cambridge,
                             1946.

SYKES, E.   *Dictionary of Non-Classical Mythology*   London, 1961.

TERRA, HELMUT DE   *Man and Mammoth in Mexico*   London, 1957.
THOMSON, W. M.   *The Land and the Book*   London, 1877.
TYRRELL, G. W.   *The Earth and its Mysteries*   London, 1953.

UNGER, M. F.   *Bible Dictionary*   Chicago, 1957.

VAILLANT, G. C.   *The Aztecs of Mexico*   London, 1950.
VELIKOVSKY, I.   *Earth in Upheaval*   New York, 1955.

WHEELER, R. E. M.   *Early India and Pakistan*   London, 1959.
WILLS, L. J.   *A Palaeogeographical Atlas of the British Isles and parts of Europe*   London, 1951.
WISEMAN, D. J.   *Illustrations from Biblical Archaeology*   London, 1963.
WISEMAN, P. J.   *New Discoveries in Babylonia about Genesis* London, n.d.
WOOLDRIDGE, S. W. and   *An Outline of Geomorphology*   London, 1959.
   MORGAN, R. S.
WOOLLEY, C. L.   *A Forgotten Kingdom*   London, 1953.
WOOLLEY, C. L.   *Excavations at Ur*   London, 1963.
WRIGHT, G. F.   *Scientific Confirmations of the Old Testament History*   London, 1907.
WRIGHT, W. B.   *The Quaternary Ice Age*   London, 1937.

YOUNG, E. J.   *An Introduction to the Old Testament*   London, 1949.
YOUNG, J. Z.   *The Life of the Vertebrates*   Oxford, 1962.

ZEUNER, F. E.   *Dating the Past*   London, 1958.

INDEX OF SUBJECTS

INDEX OF NAMES